IN A FIT OF LAUGHTER

IN
A FIT
OF
LAUGHTER

AN ANTHOLOGY OF MODERN HUMOR

Edited by Veronica Geng

With an Introduction by Steve Allen

Jacket Illustration by Richard Smith

PLATT & MUNK, PUBLISHERS

NEW YORK

ACKNOWLEDGMENTS

The editor is grateful to the authors, agents, and publishers listed below for permission to reprint selections in this volume.

"TELEPHONE" from *The Telephone* by Mike Nichols and Elaine May, copyright © 1960, 1969 by Mike Nichols and Elaine May. Reprinted by permission of the authors.

"UNHAPPY FRANK" from *In His Own Write* by John Lennon, copyright © 1964 by John Lennon. Reprinted by permission of Simon & Schuster, Inc., New York, and Jonathan Cape Ltd., London.

"DENTAL OR MENTAL, I SAY IT'S SPINACH" from *The Most of S. J. Perelman* by S. J. Perelman, copyright 1958 by S. J. Perelman. Reprinted by permission of the author.

"WHAT SHOULD CHILDREN TELL PARENTS?" by E. B. White from *Is Sex Necessary?* by James Thurber and E. B. White. Copyright, 1929 by Harper & Brothers; renewed 1957 by James Thurber and E. B. White. Reprinted by permission of Harper & Row, Publishers.

"THE ETIQUETTE OF COURTSHIP" from *Perfect Behavior,* by Donald Ogden Stewart. Copyright 1922 by George H. Doran Company; copyright renewed 1950 by Donald Ogden Stewart. Reprinted by permission of the author.

"THE LATE-SHOW PITCHMAN" from *Bigger Than a Breadbox* by Steve Allen, with a Commentary by Leonard Feather. Copyright © 1967 by Steve Allen. Reprinted by permission of Doubleday & Company, Inc.

"THE DISCOVERY OF AMERICA" from *It All Started with Columbus* by Richard Armour. Copyright © 1961 by Richard Armour. Reprinted by permission of McGraw-Hill Book Company.

"THE CASE OF DOC GREEN" from *The Rivercliff Golf Killings* by Don Marquis, copyright 1927 by Don Marquis, from *The Best of Don Marquis.* Reprinted by permission of Doubleday & Company, Inc.

"CHAPTER THE LAST: MERRIMAN EXPLAINS" by Alex Atkinson. © Punch Publications, London. Reprinted by permission of Punch Publications.

"THE COLOR OF MICE" by E. B. White from the September 22, 1928 issue of *The New Yorker*. Reprinted by permission; Copyright © 1928, 1956 The New Yorker Magazine, Inc.

"MY FINANCIAL CAREER" from *Laugh with Leacock* by Stephen Leacock. Copyright 1930 by Dodd, Mead & Company, Inc. Copyright renewed 1958 by George Leacock. Reprinted by permission of Dodd, Mead & Company, Inc.

CONTENTS

INTRODUCTION

I don't know who the young fellow was who said, several years ago, "Don't trust anybody over thirty," but he's probably over thirty by now himself, what with everything happening so fast these days.

Whatever his age, his advice was absurd, as either a moment's serious reflection or the perusal of this book will suggest. Most of the authors represented herein are old enough to be your grandfather, and knowing the personal habits of some of them I wouldn't be surprised if they were.

But all seriousness aside, this delicious collection of comic stories makes two things clear: (a) (or 1, if you prefer) the best humor is timeless and (b) (or 2) people don't get especially funny till they're past thirty. At least on paper.

The present young generation has produced some interesting poets, a number of gifted composers and lyricists, quite a few fine, sensitive singers, and some very loud guitar players, but—for what reason I do not know—it has yet to produce a crop of representative humorists.

The young, therefore, when in the mood for commercially marketed humor, have to turn to funny movies, TV comedy shows, *Mad* magazine, or books such as this, all of which are produced by men whose age would make them look decidedly out of place at a love-in, riot, protest march or rock concert.

Oh, there's a third thing that this anthology establishes: that it is possible to be brilliantly amusing without references to sex or scatology. To the extent that there is anything at all uniquely identifiable as The New Humor it is, I'm sorry to have to say, not new at all but is rather derived from three main streams of influence. The first of these is the Lenny Bruce–Mort Sahl school of social commentary, which bloomed in the mid-50's; the second is the kind of mixed satire-and-slapstick originally popularized on TV in the early 50's by Sid Caesar, Ernie Kovacs and your obedient servant (the sort of thing seen on "Laugh-In" and The Smothers Brothers and Carol Burnett shows) ; and the third is simply the ever-popular Dirty Joke, time of origin unknown.

One can honestly envy the young reader who is about to *discover* Benchley, Thurber, Perelman, Leacock and the other giants. I still recall the giddy feeling of learning—at the age of fifteen—that Robert Benchley walked my planet in my time. I first got hooked on his marvelous short comedy movies, graduated to his books, and spent the next quarter-century haunting bookstores, intent on locating his every published work.

Explanatory introductions to anthologies sometimes undertake to explain, to decipher, what the reader is about to enjoy. Forget it. There is no explaining humor, in the truest sense. All the great philosophers have made the attempt, but there is wide disagreement among them about the phenomenon.

Some have said that surprise is the one essential ingredient of a comic statement, but any young person who has listened to a Bill Cosby album fourteen times knows that's not true. Others have suggested that all laughter is at base sadistic but the innocent giggling of small children disproves the contention. Some moderns feel that the only humor worth the name is bitter satire that comments on the social predicament of man, but if this were true why would we laugh at a witty pun by Dick Cavett, a naughty leer by Johnny Carson, or a man with a German army helmet saying "Very interesting"?

One odd thing about humor is that it is quite a trick to write about it in a humorous way. The magic of the thing seems to disappear under analysis and one is left with a puff of dry dust.

Another peculiarity of the art form is that no two humorists or comedians are funny in precisely the same way. We laugh at W. C. Fields on the Late Show for reasons quite different than those which convince us that Pat Paulsen is amusing. Thomas Meehan's delightfully silly "Yma Dream" will make you laugh aloud, but not for the same reasons that you will chuckle at Frank Sullivan's perceptive delineation of journalistic and political clichés.

While I am sure that Carl Reiner, Mel Brooks, Mike Nichols, Elaine May and I are equally honored to be included among such distinguished company I am not sure that—with the possible exception of Benchley—the performing humorist is ever truly represented by a printed presentation of his comedy routines. In any event perhaps it will help, in reading "The Late-Show Pitchman," "The 2000-Year-Old Man" and "Telephone," if the reader keeps in mind that these pieces were designed to be heard rather than read.

The best humor, in my opinion, is found in the frequently tragic reality of human experience. A frightened woman actually phoned the Los Angeles Police Department not long ago and in a distracted whisper said, "There's a prowler in my back yard!"

The officer on switchboard duty asked the caller for her address. There was a moment's pause and then the woman said, "I'd better not give it to you; I don't want to get involved."

Then there was the time the late Senator Joseph McCarthy emerged from a congressional committee room in high dudgeon. Reporters asked him to comment on a startling allegation that had just been made. "Why," McCarthy spluttered, in all seriousness, "it's the most unheard-of thing I've ever heard of."

No one can write funnier lines than these, but there aren't enough of them to go around; and most of us don't recognize them when we hear them. So we are richly fortunate in being able to enjoy the writings of that small company of professional humorists whose most important service, perhaps, is to assist man in retaining his sanity in a troubled world.

Encino, California, 1969

IN A FIT OF LAUGHTER

MIKE NICHOLS
and ELAINE MAY

Telephone

"Telephone" was created by Nichols and May and also performed by them as a skit in their Broadway show, "An Evening with Mike Nichols and Elaine May." Mr. Nichols played the harassed caller, and Miss May played all the female roles.

(MAN *enters pay telephone booth and dials* "O.")

MAN: (*humming under breath*) Bum-pa dum-da-dum . . .

OPERATOR: (*nasally*) Informay-shun.

MAN: Operator, get me the number please of George Kaplan, K-A-P-L-A-N, at 4411 Huguenot Walloon Drive.

OPERATOR: That is George Kap-lan—

MAN: Yes, that's right.

OPERATOR: —that is Kap-lan—

MAN: Mmm-hmm, yes.

OPERATOR: —that is K as in knife, A as in aardvaark, P as in pneumonia, L as in luscious, A as in aardvaark again, N as in newel post, Kap-lan?

MAN: Ah, I *think* so, yes.

OPERATOR: Just one mo-ment. I will look that number up for you.

MAN: Right, thank you very much. . . . (*Pause*) Uh, operator, if you could try to hurry up a little bit I am—

OPERATOR: I *am*. I'm looking the number up for you.

MAN: I know, I know, I know, I don't mean to rush you at all, it's just that I'm terrifically late and I've got—

OPERATOR: That number is listed in your directory.

MAN: Operator, there is *no* directory here, I swear to God.

OPERATOR: Will you please take a pencil—

MAN: Yes—

OPERATOR: —and write the number dow-un?

MAN: Yes. I promise. I definitely will, yes.

OPERATOR: That number is Fairfax 9—

MAN: HELLO? HELLO? Operator, hello?—

OPERATOR: Informay-shun.

MAN: —hello, op-op-op-operator—

OPERATOR: Informay-shun.

MAN: You collected my dime!

OPERATOR: Informay-shun is a free service, sir. When you hang up, your dime will be returned to you.

MAN: Ye—miss, listen I-I—I *know* it's usually a free service, see, the thing is in this case I heard the dime, you know, hit all those other dimes? See? I—I *know it's in there*—and *I* wouldn't bother you about a *dime,* operator. In this case, miss, it's my last dime, I have no change, my *car* has broken down, and I'm an hour late for a very important appointment, so you can see th—HELLO?

OPERATOR: Informay-shun.

MAN: Oh no . . .

OPERATOR: Yes?

MAN: Miss, please return my dime!

OPERATOR: Sir, I cannot return your dime to you until you hang up, and when you hang up your dime will be returned to you.

MAN: No, it *won't*, operator, listen to me, I *know that sound*, I've heard it all my life! That dime is *in* there.

OPERATOR: Informay-shun cannot ar-gue with a closed mind.

MAN: Ohhhhh . . .

OPERATOR: Why don't you try hang-ing up?

MAN: Because . . . I can't take the chance! I—I'll lose the dime, I'll lose you. . . . Look, miss, ca—can I go over your head? Is there someone else I can speak to? A human?

OPERATOR: You wish to speak to a hu-man?

MAN: Yes!

OPERATOR: About your alleg-ed dime?

MAN: It's a *real dime!*

OPERATOR: Just one mo-ment. I will connect you with the informay-shun super-visor.

MAN: Oh thank you very much. . . . HELLO? MISS? OPERATOR? HELLO?

OPERATOR: Informay-shun.

MAN: Ah, listen, there's, there's no chance that you would, say, jostle something with your elbow and just cut me off completely?

OPERATOR: We do not work with our elbows, sir.

(*Pause*)

MAN: Oh come on, come on. . . .

SUPERVISOR: Information supervisor. Can I help you?

MAN: Uh, I—I sincerely hope so.

SUPERVISOR: Yes, sir.

MAN: Uh, just a minute ago, operator—

SUPERVISOR: *Supervisor*. I'm the information *super*visor.

MAN: Oh, oh I'm sorry—

SUPERVISOR: Oh, that's all right—

MAN: Uh, just a minute ago one of your girls inadvertently collected my last dime, and you see as I explained to her, my car—

SUPERVISOR: Oh no sir. Now you see, sir, information doesn't charge a dime, you see. No—

MAN: Yeh, yeh, no, look, miss, I've already gone through—no, the oth—the other girl—and I—

SUPERVISOR: —you see, when you hang up, you see, your dime will be returned to you. Information is a completely free service.

MAN: NOT TONIGHT! Now miss, please, try to understand what I'm saying to you, I—I'm speaking as one human being to another. For*get* that you're an operator!

SUPERVISOR: I'm a *supervisor,* I'm the information supervisor.

MAN: Oh, all right, fine, all right, *supervisor,* Bell Telephone has stolen my last dime, that's what it comes down to—and, well, you *stole* it, I put it in the telephone and you took it away—

SUPERVISOR: Well now just a minute sir, I mean just a minute. You know, Bell Telephone wouldn't *steal* your dime you know—

MAN: —it's, it's my—it's—well of course miss—they they they
have stolen my dime—yeh, I—I—Oh, I know, that's exactly
my point—yeh, I know, yeh—right, right—well—

SUPERVISOR: I mean, Bell Telephone doesn't *need* your dime,
Bell Telephone gets millions of dimes every day, they
wouldn't pick out *your* dime to *steal,* you know.

MAN: —they stole it, dammit, they stole it!

SUPERVISOR: Huh, I'm not going to sit here and argue with
you—

MAN: Well, now miss, look, I—

SUPERVISOR: —I mean, if you mean to sit there and tell me
you think Bell Telephone has *stolen* your *dime—*

MAN: That is what I've been telling you now for twenty
minutes.

SUPERVISOR: Well I'll be very happy to return your dime to
you.

(Pause)

MAN: You will?

SUPERVISOR: Yes.

MAN: Ahh, thank you. Thank you very much.

SUPERVISOR: Not at all. What is your name and address?

(Pause)

MAN: Miss. . .?

SUPERVISOR: Yes?

MAN: You're, uh, you're going to send me a *whole lot of
stamps,* aren't you.

SUPERVISOR: Yes we are, mmm-hmmm, that's right.

MAN: Yes, I knew it. Look, I've received—I've received
stamps from you people in the past, and it's a swell sur-

prise. . . . I *need the dime now.* Look, can I—can I go over your head? Is there someone else I can speak to?

SUPERVISOR: Well, I could connect you with the managing supervisor, Miss Jones, who wouldn't be able to help you either, heh-heh. . . . If you want to give it a whirl . . .

MAN: Yes!

SUPERVISOR: Just hold the line.

MAN: Miss Jones. Please. And please hurry.

(Pause)

MISS JONES: *(in soft seductive voice)* Managing supervisor Miss Jones. Can I help you?

MAN: Oh, Miss Jones! I—I'm so glad I finally got ahold of you.

MISS JONES: What *is* it sir?

MAN: Miss Jones—This is my story!

MISS JONES: Yes, sir, I'm here. . . .

MAN: Ohhhhhh, Miss Jones, uh *(he begins to cry)* a *long time ago* one of your operators inadvertently collected my last dime.

MISS JONES: Oh my God!

MAN: Yes. And *(sob)* you see, as—as I explained to her it's like this *(sob)* . . . I'm sorry, Miss Jones, I don't usually do this. . . .

MISS JONES: No sir, you go ahead and cry.

MAN: Thank you. . . .

MISS JONES: Oh, Bell Telephone understands.

MAN: You're very kind.

MISS JONES: Well, you've lost your dime.

MAN: No, she *took* it, and I have to have it back.

MISS JONES: Of *course* you do, sir, and Bell Telephone will be very happy to give you a free call for that dime.

MAN: Oh, Miss Jones—

MISS JONES: Yes, sir?

MAN: —if—if this is true, I'll never forget you as long as I live.

MISS JONES: Well it's true.

MAN: Oh thank you, thank you, thank you Miss Jones, thank you—

MISS JONES: Oh no no no no no no no—

MAN: Thank you.

MISS JONES: Our pleasure to serve you. You just give me the number you're calling.

(*Long pause*)

MAN: Miss Jones.

MISS JONES: Yes sir?

MAN: Ah, you're dealing here with an ass. Ah, you see, she took the dime before I ever got the number. Look, we'll forget it, I'll lose my job that's all—

MISS JONES: Sir, there's—there's—there's no need to take that attitude—

MAN: No?

MISS JONES: Not at all. You can simply give me the name of the party you're calling—

MAN: Oh!

MISS JONES: —and I can look that number up for you.

MAN: Grand. The name is George Kaplan, K-A-P-L-A-N as in newel post?

MISS JONES: One moment.

MAN: Yes . . .

MISS JONES: Hello sir! I have that number for you!

MAN: Yes? Yes, Miss Jones yes?

MISS JONES: That number is Fairfax 9-1975—

MAN: —1975 tell me what to do!

MISS JONES: Hold onto your receiver—

MAN: Right, check, right, right—

MISS JONES: —until you hear the dial tone!

MAN: —wait, wait for the dial tone—

MISS JONES: Then dial your number, sir—

MAN: —dial as I ordinarily would—

MISS JONES: You have a FREE CALL!

MAN: Thank you Miss Jones, I'll *never forget you!* . . .
    (*Dials.*) . . . seven . . . five . . .
(*Pause*)

VOICE: This—is—a—recording.—You—have—dialled—a—wrong—
exchange.

NICHOLS and MAY—like ham and eggs, shoes and socks, or Simon and Garfunkel—were an unbeatable combination. They were born a year apart: he in 1931 in Berlin, Germany; she in 1932 in Philadelphia. They met at the University of Chicago. Both were interested in acting. Mr. Nichols had studied in New York at the Actors Studio with Lee Strasberg. Elaine May came from a theatrical family—her father was an actor in the Yiddish theater. From 1954 to 1957 the two performed at a Chicago theater called the Compass. The acting at the Compass was improvised. That is, members of the audience suggested a situation, or a line, or a character, and the actors used the suggestion to make up a skit on the spot. Nichols and May raised improvisation from an exercise to an art. Not only were they excellent actors, but they created wildly funny material, usually poking fun at some idiocy of modern life. Sample: starlet being interviewed by a radio announcer: "Albert Schweitzer? Well, I never dated Al personally. . . ."

In 1957 Nichols and May, with four other actors, came to New York City and played with great success in nightclubs. In 1960 they starred in a two-man Broadway show, *An Evening with Mike Nichols and Elaine May*. Since then they have separated. Mr. Nichols is a sought-after director whose credits include several Broadway hits, and the films *Who's Afraid of Virginia Woolf?*, *The Graduate*, and *Catch-22*. Miss May has acted in the films *Luv* and *Enter Laughing*, and wrote and directed a play, *Adaptation*.

An Evening with Mike Nichols and Elaine May is available on a long-playing record.

JOHN LENNON

Unhappy Frank

Frank looked at the table hardly daring to look at the table. "I hate that table," he said "Bloody owld table in my house." Then he looked at the clock. "Damn that clock in my house," said Frank, for it was his house you know. After a little bit his eye came across his very mother's chair. "Don't like that chair one bit," he showbedy. "Just look at that garbet all filby and durby. How am I supposed to look affaffter all this garby ruddish. Wart am I but a slave tow look upon with deesekfrebit all the peegle larfing and buzing me in front of all the worled. How can I but garry on? How? Hab I no live of my own to do but wart I must ever jub gleenig and looking areftor theese damn owld house of my own?" Frank went over to his dubb old mother, whomn was stikl liffing with him. "What are you larfing at you dubb owld boot?"

"Havn' I nuff treble without you kakking in the korber?" With that Frank stub up and kicked her plainly on the head. "Take that for larfing you budd oled griff." "I hate that boot," he said smiling quirkley to themselves.

"I'm going to sell this daft shed and you to aswell, also Mummy."

So he sold it all and left the country and settled down in another country which he did not like half as much as his dear old home in England with his dear old quaint old luvly mother what he (Frank) lost due to a bad harvest. Which judd go to show what happens.

JOHN LENNON wrote his first book when he was seven: "Sport, Speed and Illustrated. Edited and Illustrated by J. W. Lennon." It was a collection of jokes, drawings, and an original serial story that ended each installment with "If you liked this, come again next week. It'll be even better." He also showed early talent in a money-begging postcard: "Funs are getting low."

John Lennon was born on October 9, 1940, in Liverpool, during an air raid. His parents separated when he was a boy, and he was raised by his Aunt Mimi, known for her famous last words, "A guitar's all right, John, but you'll never earn your living by it." At Liverpool's Quarry Bank High School, John Lennon led several other long-haired fans of American rock music in forming a pop group called the Quarrymen. With changes in personnel, the Quarrymen evolved into the Moondogs, the Silver Beatles, and finally the Beatles: John, Paul, George, and Ringo.

With Paul McCartney, John Lennon has written most of the songs recorded by the Beatles. He has also produced two books of writings and drawings—*In His Own Write* and *A Spaniard in the Works*—leading his friend Paul to ponder, "Is he deep? Is he arty, with it, or cultured?" *You might well arsk.*

S. J. PERELMAN

Dental or Mental, I Say It's Spinach

A few days ago, under the heading, MAN LEAPS OUT WINDOW
AS DENTIST GETS FORCEPS, *The New York Times* reported
the unusual case of a man who leaped out a window as the
dentist got the forceps. Briefly, the circumstances were these.
A citizen in Staten Island tottered into a dental parlor and,
indicating an aching molar, moaned, "It's killing me. You've
got to pull it out." The dentist grinned like a Cheshire cat—
The New York Times neglected to say so, but a Cheshire cat
who was present at the time grinned like a dentist—and
reached for his instruments. "There was a leap and a crash,"
continues the account. "The astonished dentist saw his patient spring through the closed window and drop ten feet to
the sidewalk, where he lay dazed." The casualty was subse-

quently treated at a nearby hospital for abrasion and shock by Drs. J. G. Abrazian and Walter Shock, and then, like a worm, crept back to the dentist, apologized and offered to pay for the damage. On one point, however, he remained curiously adamant. He still has his tooth.

As a party who recently spent a whole morning with his knees braced against a dentist's chest, whimpering "Don't—don't—I'll do anything, but don't drill!" I am probably the only man in America equipped to sympathize with the poor devil. Ever since Nature presented me at birth with a set of thirty-two flawless little pearls of assorted sizes, I never once relaxed my vigilant stewardship of same. From the age of six onward, I constantly polished the enamel with peanut brittle, massaged the incisors twice daily with lollipops, and chewed taffy and chocolate-covered caramels faithfully to exercise the gums. As for consulting a dentist regularly, my punctuality practically amounted to a fetish. Every twelve years I would drop whatever I was doing and allow wild Caucasian ponies to drag me to a reputable orthodontist. I guess you might say I was hipped on the subject of dental care.

When, therefore, I inadvertently stubbed a tooth on a submerged cherry in an old-fashioned last week and my toupee ricocheted off the ceiling, I felt both dismayed and betrayed. By eleven the next morning, I was seated in the antechamber of one Russell Pipgrass, D.D.S., limply holding a copy of the *National Geographic* upside down and pretending to be absorbed in Magyar folkways. Through the door communicating with the arena throbbed a thin, blood-curdling whine like a circular saw biting into a green plank. Suddenly an ear-splitting shriek rose above it, receding into a choked gurgle. I nonchalantly tapped out my cigarette in my eardrum and leaned over to the nurse; a Medusa type with serpents writhing out from under her prim white coif.

"Ah—er—pardon me," I observed, swallowing a bit of emery paper I had been chewing. "Did you hear anything just then?"

"Why, no," she replied, primly tucking back a snake under her cap. "What do you mean?"

"A—kind of a scratchy sound," I faltered.

"Oh, that," she sniffed carelessly. "Impacted wisdom tooth. We have to go in through the skull for those, you know." Murmuring some inconsequential excuse about lunching with a man in Sandusky, Ohio, I dropped to the floor and was creeping toward the corridor on all fours when Dr. Pipgrass emerged, rubbing his hands. "Well, here's an unexpected windfall!" he cackled, his eyes gleaming with cupidity. "Look out—slam the door on him!" Before I could dodge past, he pinioned me in a hammer lock and bore me, kicking and struggling, into his web. He was trying to wrestle me into the chair when the nurse raced in, brandishing a heavy glass ash tray.

"Here, hit him with this!" she panted.

"No, no, we mustn't bruise him," muttered Pipgrass. "Their relatives always ask a lot of silly questions." They finally made me comfy by strapping me into the chair with a half a dozen towels, tilted my feet up and pried open my teeth with a spoon. "Now then, where are his X-rays?" demanded the doctor.

"We haven't any," returned the nurse. "This is the first time he's been here."

"Well, bring me any X-rays," her employer barked. "What difference does it make? When you've seen one tooth, you've seen them all." He held up the X-rays against the light and examined them critically. "Well, friend, you're in a peck of trouble," he said at length. "You may as well know the worst. These are the teeth of an eighty-year-old man. You got here just in time." Plucking a horrendous nozzle from the rack, he shot compressed air down my gullet that sent me into a strangled paroxysm, and peered curiously at my inlays.

"Who put those in, a steamfitter?" he sneered. "You ought to be arrested for walking around with a job like that." He turned abruptly at the rustle of greenbacks and glared at his nurse. "See here, Miss Smedley, how many times have I told you not to count the patient's money in front of him? Take the wallet outside and go through it there." She nodded shamefacedly and slunk out. "That's the kind of thing that creates a bad impression on the layman," growled Dr. Pipgrass, poking at my tongue with a sharp stick. "Now what seems to be the trouble in there?"

"Ong ong ong," I wheezed.

"H'm'm'm, a cleft palate," he mused. "Just as I feared. And you've got between four and five thousand cavities. While we're at it, I think we'd better tear out those lowers with a jackhammer and put in some nice expensive crowns. Excuse me." He quickly dialed a telephone number. "Is that you, Irene?" he asked. "Russell. Listen, on that white mink coat we were talking about at breakfast—go right ahead, I've changed my mind. . . . No, I'll tell you later. He's filthy with it."

"Look, Doctor," I said with a casual yawn. "It's nothing really—just a funny tickling sensation in that rear tooth. I'll be back Tuesday—a year from Tuesday."

"Yes, yes," he interrupted, patting me reassuringly.

"Don't be afraid now; this won't hurt a bit." With a slow, cunning smile, he produced from behind his back a hypodermic of the type used on brewery horses and, distending my lip, plunged it into the gum. The tip of my nose instantly froze, and my tongue took on the proportions of a bolt of flannel. I tried to cry out, but my larynx was out to lunch. Seizing the opportunity, Pipgrass snatched up his drill, took a firm purchase on my hair and teed off. A mixture of sensation roughly comparable to being alternately stilettoed and inflated with a bicycle pump overcame me; two thin wisps of smoke curled upward slowly from my ears. Fortunately, I had been schooled from boyhood to withstand pain without flinching, and beyond an occasional scream that rattled the windows, I bore myself with the stoicism of a red man. Scarcely ninety minutes later, Dr. Pipgrass thrust aside the drill, wiped his streaming forehead and shook the mass of protoplasm before him.

"Well, we're in the home stretch," he announced brightly, extracting a rubber sheet from a drawer. "We'll put this dam on you and fill her in a jiffy. You don't get claustrophobia, do you?"

"Wh-what's that?" I squeaked.

"Fear of being buried alive," he explained smoothly. "Kind of a stifling feeling. Your heart starts racing and you think you're going crazy. Pure imagination, of course." He pinned the rubber sheet over my face, slipped it over the tooth and left me alone with my thoughts. In less time than it takes to relate, I was a graduate member, *summa cum laude,* of the Claustrophobia Club. My face had turned a stunning shade of green, my heart was going like Big Ben, and a set of castanets in my knees was playing the "Malagueña." Summoning my last reserves of strength, I cast off my bonds and catapulted through the anteroom to freedom. I bequeathed Pipgrass a fleece-lined overcoat worth sixty-eight dollars, and he's welcome to it; I'll string along nicely with this big wad of chewing gum over my tooth. On me it looks good.

S. J. PERELMAN (known to his dry-cleaner as Mr. Pearlman, Mr. Perleman, or Mr. Perlman) has been one of America's top humorists since the 1930's. Today he is without a doubt the King. He would probably not like being called the King of anything —he has described himself as "button-cute, rapier-keen, wafer-thin, and pauper-poor." But as Dorothy Parker wrote, "Robert Benchley, who was probably nearest to Perelman, and Ring Lardner, who was nearest to nobody, are gone, and so Mr. Perelman stands by himself."

S. J. Perelman grew up in Providence, Rhode Island. In 1921 he entered Brown University, flinging himself into his studies of Erich von Stroheim movies and attending dances given by the Brown Christian Association, where, in his own words, "at frequent intervals, noisily advertising an overpowering thirst, I retired to a cloakroom with several other blades and choked down a minute quantity of gin, warmed to body heat, from a pocket flask." He also worked on the university's humor magazine, *The Brown Jug,* as a cartoonist, humorist, and writer of fiery editorials "advocating, of course, the dismissal of the dean and all the other pompous old foofs on the faculty." After graduation he went to work for two now-defunct humor magazines, *Judge* and *College Humor.*

In 1930 Mr. Perelman met the Marx Brothers and coauthored two of their movies, *Monkey Business* and *Horsefeathers.* Sample dialogue:

Secretary: Jennings is waxing wroth outside.

Groucho: Well, tell Roth to wax Jennings for a while.

Mr. Perelman's other assignments in Hollywood included "distilling a scenario from *How to Win Friends and Influence People.*" He admits having worked on *Sweethearts* for Jeanette MacDonald and Nelson Eddy, although later he scissored his name from the credits. Finally, irritable from increasing leisure time and sallow-faced from a diet of nutburgers, he returned to New York. Since then, his chief contribution to Hollywood has been his Academy-Award-winning screenplay for *Around the World in 80 Days.* He has also written plays—singlehanded, with his wife, and with Ogden Nash.

In 1934 Mr. Perelman's stories (they are not really stories; it is difficult to know what to call them; he calls them "needle-work") began to appear in *The New Yorker.*

S. J. Perelman has numerous imitators, but none of them have his withering scorn, his immense vocabulary of clichés, his ability to "burst into racking sobs," or his genius for fashioning long, upsetting opening sentences: "The hands of the clock pointed to one-thirty the other day, and my own, more flaccid than vermicelli, dangled inertly beside the dental chair as Dr. Yankwich shoved aside his drill, fired alternate rounds of compressed air and raspberry shrub down my throat, and straightened up. 'There—wasn't it a breeze?' he asked gaily."

The biggest collection of S. J. Perelman's work is *The Most of S. J. Perelman,* 650 pages of his writing from 1930 to 1958, with an introduction by Dorothy Parker.

E. B. WHITE

What Should Children Tell Parents?

So many children have come to me and said, "What shall I tell my parents about sex?" My answer is always the same: "Tell them the truth. If the subject is approached in a tactful way, it should be no more embarrassing to teach a parent about sex than to teach him about personal pronouns. And it should be less discouraging."

In discussing sex enlightenment for parents, first of all, definitions are needed. What do we mean by "parents"? Do we mean all adults who have had children? Do we mean adults who have had children, they knew not why? Or do we mean married people who have given birth to one or more offspring but have never gone into the matter very thoroughly? For the purposes of this article, it will be assumed that by "parents" we mean all adult persons permeated with a strong sense of indecency.

I have talked with hundreds of children about the problem of educating their parents along sex lines. So many of them have told me that they honestly tried to give their elders the benefit of their rich experience in life, but that the parents usually grew flushed and red and would reply, "Nice people don't talk about such things." It is true that a great gap exists between generations. The fact that children are embarrassed to have their parents along when they are attending certain movies or plays is indicative of how hard it is to overcome the old fear of allowing one's elders to learn anything. A child never knows at what point in a play his uninformed old father will start to giggle. It is hard for children to break through and really come in touch with their elders. "Nice people don't talk about such things!" is the defense which old people put up against life itself, when they feel it crowding in all around their heads. Parents hesitate to discuss things calmly and intelligently with their children for two reasons: first, they have a kind of dread of learning something they don't want to know; and second, they feel that if they must learn anything at all they would like to be spared the humiliation of learning it from their offspring. Actually, middle age (and even senescence) is marked by a great curiosity about life. There is a feeling that life is slipping away quickly, and that it would be terrible to have the end come before everything in life has been revealed. The beauty of life, always apparent, implies a mystery which is disturbing right up to the bitter end. The spectacle of old men wistfully attending sex lectures (as they frequently do) suggests that the strong suspicion exists in them that somewhere they will hear the magic word by which human affairs will become clarified, somewhere they will glimpse the ultimate ecstasy. Children who allow their fathers and mothers, to whom they owe their very existence, to go on wondering about sex, are derelicts to duty.

If young folks lack the tact or intelligence requisite to enlightening their parents, the task should be intrusted to someone else. Yet it is hard to say to whom. A child should think twice before sending his father around to public school to secure sex information from his teacher. Women teachers, to borrow a phrase, are apt to be "emotionally illiterate." Many teachers have had no sex life and are just waiting for somebody like your father to show up.

One's father and mother are never too old to be told facts. Indeed, it is most unkind to keep them in ignorance and allow them to nourish the doubts and horrors of their imagination. The majority of parents pick up their knowledge of the facts of life from smoking-car conversations, bridge-club teas, and after-dinner speakers. They receive it from their vicious adult companions who are only slightly less ignorant than they are and who give them a hopelessly garbled version. They pick it up, too, from the gutter.

This matter of picking up information from the gutter is an interesting topic in itself. Quite the most remarkable case history that has come to my notice is that of François Delamater, a parent thirty years of age, who went deliberately to the gutter for his sex education. He had heard, as all people do hear sometime or other, that sex can be learned from the gutter, so he set out to make a comprehensive survey of the gutters of eighteen large American cities. For a long time he found out nothing, although he was a very curious man. By a

peculiar piece of fortune, however, he happened to be walking in Cincinnati one day and met a man who was leading a
tame stork. The man was in the gutter. The stork carried in
its bill a live baby, in swaddling clothes. Smelling a rat, Mr.
Delamater stopped the man and inquired where the baby
came from. The man replied that he didn't know.

"For that matter," continued Mr. Delamater, "where
does *any* baby come from?"

The man shook his head. Then he relented and told Mr.
Delamater that he had merely been hired to lead the stork
around the streets to advertise a moving picture called "Her
Husband's First-born." The whole incident so confused the
mind of the thirty-year-old parent that he eventually evolved
the strange theory that babies are born within the father, an
erroneous notion that dwarfed his emotions and modified his
character.

It is of the utmost importance, in imparting sex knowledge to one's parents that it be done in such a way as not to
engender fear or anxiety. The phraseology should be chosen
carefully, and efforts should be made to explain everything
clearly but without the use of words which have a tendency
to make old people nervous. The word "erotic" is such a word.
When it is necessary to speak of Man's erotic tendencies, it is
best to substitute another word. In the first place, an over-
whelming majority of parents do not know the exact meaning of the word "erotic," and to know an *in*exact meaning is
worse than nothing. Many are apt to confuse it vaguely with
"exotic." I have known parents to go through whole books by
authors like Havelock Ellis or Mary Ware Dennett without
understanding a single paragraph, because they thought
Man's "eroticism" referred to his desire to be in some foreign

place like Spain. Those parents that actually do detect the difference between the sound of the two words will immediately become nervous, inattentive, and dispirited. They will make some excuse to leave the room, and will wander out, probably to the ice-box to get themselves a cold snack, which they will eat while in a sulky frame of mind. Later they will look up the word in the dictionary, but will forget it by the time they hear it again in conversation or read it in print. Furthermore, all their taste for sex will be gone.

Just what to tell parents is, of course, a vital question, not to be answered dogmatically. Before a child can conscientiously approach such subjects as pedestalism, the recessive knee, begoniaism, frigidity in men, birth control, sublimation, and the swastika fixation, he must clear the boards. The simple phases of sex should be imparted in a direct manner: it is best to explain things in a matter-of-fact way, rather than resort to such cloudy analogies as birds and flowers. Strange to say, the habits of birds and flowers have done as little to clarify the human scene as almost any other two manifestations in nature. Further, there is always the danger, in setting up plant or animal life as an example, that one's parents will place a literal interpretation on things. I am thinking particularly of the case—which all sociological students know about—of Nina Sembrich, the fifteen-year-old high-school girl who attempted to impart knowledge to her father by telling him about bees. (Nina's mother was dead, or she would have told her too.) She traced, in rather minute detail, the renascence of earth in spring, the blossoming of the trees, the activity of the bees and their function in distributing the pollen, the fertilization of the seed and its growth during the warm languorous summer days, finally the fruition and harvest.

It was a beautiful story, redolent of orchards and sunny hillsides, instinct with life—a story that had a soporific effect on Mr. Sembrich, lulling him as the buzz of a bee lulls one in hot daisy fields. The upshot of it was that he gathered a rather strange impression from the narrative and somehow got the idea that to have babies you had to keep bees. He bought several hives, installing them in the little sitting-room on the second floor, where Mrs. Sembrich had kept her sewing-machine when she was alive. The acquisition of the apiary further complicated matters for Mr. Sembrich by reason of the fact that bees themselves enjoy a rather extraordinary sexual scheme—theirs is a complex society, infinitely more diverting and harder to understand than our own. Observed by a slightly nervous person who is trying to profit by a simple analogy—as Mr. Sembrich was—bees are capable of causing the utmost confusion.

If you will recall what you know about bees, you will readily understand what I mean. In a colony of bees, certain individuals have no sex whatsoever; these are the "workers." The male bees are "drones." The queen (or "mother") bee develops her sexual character only after being arbitrarily chosen for the purpose, walled up, and fattened on special food. Mr. Sembrich marveled at these things.

Basing his hopes entirely on what he had seen, he made his first overt act, which was to give up his business (he was a merchant tailor) on the assumption that to be endowed with masculine characteristics one had to be a drone. In this, of course, he was justified to some degree; for it is quite true that very busy men rarely are fully equipped for a complete or happy sex life. Businessmen commonly find a vicarious gratification for their erotic nature in card index systems. Often, their satiable appetite for life is dissipated in the process of dictating a single sales letter. Only men who devote virtually their entire attention to love ever glimpse its full glory or experience its bewildering intensity. (And *they* make so little money they might just as well not.)

Mr. Sembrich, therefore, was not without justification in becoming a drone, since life was what he wanted to find out about. But it was when he undertook to fatten up a lady of his acquaintance into a "mother" that he ran into difficulties. He locked her in the kitchen and plied her with rich desserts. He even urged honey on her—a rather literal expedient even for a man in his mental condition. The lady not only failed to become a mother, but she took sick and died, surrounded by a group of Mr. Sembrich's "workers," whom he had hired to help feed her. With a dead woman in the kitchen and a lot of bees upstairs in the sitting-room, the household became unbearable as a place to live and bring up his daughter Nina, so Mr. Sembrich fled, still ignorant of the essential knowledge of life.[1]

Another case, not exactly paralleling the Sembrich affair, is the case of two parents who failed to learn something to their advantage because they happened to be at dinner. It happened this way. Charles Updegraff had sent his son, Junior, to spend the summer at a boys' camp. There in addition to learning how to swim, paddle, and make fires, Junior learned about sex, so that he returned home fine and brown and a credit to the Updegraffs. (The Updegraffs had swum, paddled, made fires, and so on, for generations.) Now, at

---

1 Sexually speaking.

Camp Whortleberry (that was the name of the camp) the authorities had adopted what is known as the "pet method" for imparting sex knowledge to the boys. Each boy was given charge of a pet of some kind, and the pets were given *carte blanche*. Junior Updegraff drew a pair of sunfish. To augment the actual pet study, the boys were also given lectures by the camp director, who knew in a general way what he was talking about. Thus, when the summer was over the boys' minds were full of a strange assortment of facts and oddments, some of them rather amusing. Young Junior had hardly been home an hour when he thought he would do his old man a good turn by telling him what he knew about sunfish. The Updegraffs were at table.

"Pop," he said, "do you want the lowdown on a sunfish?"

Mrs. Updegraff hastily interrupted. "Better wait till after dinner, son," she said.

(Note: parents have always been held back by the superstitious idea that it is wrong to learn anything while eating.)

"What's the matter with right now?" asked Junior. "I was just going to tell Pop about our pet study course. I know a lot of things."

"Wait till we're through eating," said Mrs. Updegraff.

"Why should I? A mouse is an embryo twenty days, a lopsided apple is that way because it's been fertilized only on one side, male animals grow bright colored in the mating season, and so it goes. Sunfish . . ."

"Junior!" said Mrs. Updegraff, sharply. "Not till after dinner. Sunfish can wait!"

"No they can't!" cried Junior, warming up to his subject. "The father sunfish makes the nest, then . . ."

"We don't want to hear about it," snapped Junior's mother. "Tell us about your canoe trips."

"I never went on no canoe trips."

"Why not?"

"Always was watching the sunfish."

The matter was dropped and the meal continued in silence. After dinner Mr. Updegraff, secretly very much interested, hung around in the hope that his son would again open up the subject of sunfish. The boy never did. He was only a child and children are easily discouraged.

I suspect that the church is responsible, in large measure, for the ideas of life now held by adults. Sex is still sin to the evangelical clergy. A kiss is thinkable only when sanctified by the church. A child who permits his parents to continue in the belief that the elevation of the soul depends on the renunciation of the flesh is hardly doing his duty by them. Sometimes it may be advisable to quote to your parents from standard works on the subject of sex. Great care must be taken, though, to avoid abruptness, as far as possible. Thus there is some doubt in my mind whether a child ought to approach its mother on a hot afternoon when she is tired and bedraggled, and say to her: "Ma, under favorable conditions a husband and wife should remain sexually attractive to each other during the whole period of their sexual potency."

That's no way for a child to talk.

Some children have told me that instead of quoting from books they have tried leaving the books lying around, opened at pertinent pages. Even this failed to work in most cases. The mothers usually just picked up the book, dusted it, closed it, and fitted it neatly in some nearby shelf. They thought it was dusty.

E. B. WHITE, near the end of his children's book *Stuart Little,* describes a meeting between a telephone repairman and Stuart, the mouse-hero, who is journeying north. "There's something about north," says the repairman, "something that sets it apart from all other directions. A person who is heading north is not making any mistake, in my opinion."

Mr. White himself, like all philosophers worth listening to, has followed his own advice. He has been traveling due north since he started his writing career. In his early days on *The New Yorker,* he lived in New York City's Greenwich Village, later moving north—or uptown, as New Yorkers say—to a pleasant neighborhood called Turtle Bay. In 1938, "desiring to simplify my life," he left the city and went with his wife and son to live on a farm on the coast of Maine.

In his writing, Mr. White seems to follow some interior compass that points him steadily in the right direction. His writing is clear, sure, and accurate. His friend James Thurber said that his "silver and crystal sentences . . . have a ring like nobody else's sentences in the world." The pure beauty of Mr. White's northerly writing might be summed up by these words of the telephone repairman in *Stuart Little:* "Following a broken telephone line north, I have come upon some wonderful places. Swamps where cedars grow and turtles wait on logs but not for anything in particular; fields bordered by crooked fences broken by years of standing still. . . . In the north I have eaten my lunch in pastures rank with ferns and junipers, all under fair skies with a wind blowing."

E. (Elwyn) B. (Brooks) White was born in 1899 in Mount Vernon, New York. He attended public schools and then went to Cornell University. (Any Cornell student named White is always called Andy, after the university's first president, Andrew White. So E. B. White has always been Andy White to his friends and colleagues.) His education was interrupted briefly while he served in World War I. Then he returned to Cornell, edited the *Cornell Daily Sun,* and graduated.

After a few years working for a newspaper in Seattle and an advertising agency in New York City, he sent some verse and light articles to *The New Yorker.* Shortly afterward, in 1926, he was hired as a part-time editor. Later he became a full-time member of the staff. His first job was editing the "newsbreaks," strange and funny misprints from newspapers and magazines, used to fill out the bottoms of *New Yorker* columns. He also reported, wrote, rewrote other people's writing, and invented captions for cartoons. Once he even painted a cover—a seahorse wearing a feedbag on his nose. Mr. White's main contribution, however, was the "Notes and Comment" department, an editorial that opens each issue of the magazine. His writing for this feature established *The New Yorker*'s tone—a calm, quiet, witty voice.

With his wife Katharine, former literary editor of *The New Yorker,* Mr. White edited *A Subtreasury of American Humor,* probably the best collection of its kind. His essays, many of them comic accounts of his attempts as a city man to fit into country life, are collected in *One Man's Meat* and *The Points of My Compass.* His books for children (and adults) are *Stuart Little* and *Charlotte's Web.*

DONALD OGDEN STEWART

The Etiquette of Courtship

A few words about love

Courtship is one of the oldest of social customs, even antedating in some countries such long-established usages as marriage, or the wearing of white neckties with full evening dress. The beginnings of the etiquette of courtship were apparently connected in some way with the custom of "love" between the sexes, and many of the old amatory forms still survive in the modern courtship. It is generally agreed among students of the history of etiquette that when "love" first began to become popular among the better class of younger people they took to it with such avidity that it was necessary to devise some sort of rules for the conduct of formal or informal love-making. These rules, together with

various amendments, now constitute the etiquette of courtship.

Suppose, for example, that you are a young gentleman
named Richard Roe desirous of entering upon a formal
courtship with some refined young girl of fashion. You are
also, being a college graduate, engaged in the bond business.
One morning there comes into your financial institution a
young lady, named Dorothy Doe, who at once attracts your
attention by her genteel manners, as exemplified by the fact
that she calls the president of your company "father." So many
young people seem to think it "smart" to refer to their parents
as "dad" or "my old man"; you are certain, as soon as you hear
her say "Hello, father" to your employer, that she is un-
doubtedly a worthy object of courtship.

Correct Introductions: How To Make Them

Your first step should be, of course, the securing of an
introduction. Introductions still play an important part in
social intercourse, and many errors are often perpetrated by
those ignorant of *savoir faire* (correct form) . When introducing a young lady to a stranger, for example, it is not *au fait*
(correct form) to simply say, "Mr. Roe, I want you to shake
hands with my friend Dorothy." Under the rules of the *beau
monde* (correct form) this would probably be done as follows: "Dorothy (or Miss Doe) , shake hands with Mr. Roe."
Always give the name of the lady first, unless you are introducing someone to the President of the United States, the
Archbishop of Canterbury, a member of the nobility above a
baron, or a customer. The person who is being "introduced"
then extends his (or her) right ungloved hand and says,

"Shake." You "shake," saying at the same time, "It's warm (cool) for November (May) ," to which the other replies, "I'll say it is."

This brings up the interesting question of introducing two people to each other, neither of whose names you can remember. This is generally done by saying very quickly to one of the parties, "Of course you know Miss Unkunkunk." Say the last "unk" very quickly, so that it sounds like any name from Ab to Zinc. You might even sneeze violently. Of course, in nine cases out of ten, one of the two people will at once say, "I didn't get the name," at which you laugh, "Ha! Ha! Ha!" in a carefree manner several times, saying at the same time,"Well, well—so you didn't get the name—you didn't get the name—well, well." If the man still persists in wishing to know who it is to whom he is being introduced, the best procedure consists in simply braining him on the spot with a club or convenient slab of paving stone.

The "introduction," in cases where you have no mutual friend to do the introducing, is somewhat more difficult, but can generally be arranged as follows:

Procure a few feet of stout manila rope or clothes-line, from any of the better-class hardware stores. Ascertain (from the Social Register, preferably) the location of the young lady's residence, and go there on some dark evening about nine o'clock. Fasten the rope across the sidewalk in front of the residence about six inches or a foot from the ground. Then, with the aid of a match and some kerosene, set fire to the young lady's house in several places and retire behind a convenient tree. After some time, if she is at home, she will probably be forced to run out of her house to avoid being burned to death. In her excitement she will fail to notice the rope which you have stretched across the sidewalk and will fall. This is your opportunity to obtain an introduction. Stepping up to her and touching your hat politely, you say, in a well-modulated voice, "I beg your pardon, Miss Doe, but I cannot help noticing that you are lying prone on the sidewalk." If she is well-bred, she will not at first speak to you, as you are a perfect stranger. This silence, however, should be your cue to once more tip your hat and remark, "I realize, Miss Doe, that I have not had the honor of an introduction, but you will admit that you are lying prone on the sidewalk. Here is my card—and here is one for Mrs. Doe, your mother." At that you should hand her two plain engraved calling cards, each containing your name and address. If there are any other ladies in her family—aunts, grandmothers, et cetera —it is correct to leave cards for them also. Be sure that the cards are clean, as the name of the calling card is generally sufficient for identification purposes without the addition of the thumbprint.

When she has accepted your cards, she will give you one of hers, after which it will be perfectly correct for you to assist her to rise from the sidewalk. Do not, however, press your attentions further upon her at this time, but after expressing the proper regret over her misfortune it would be well to bow and retire.

Cards and Flowers

The next day, however, you should send flowers, enclosing another of your cards. It might be well to write some message on the card recalling the events of the preceding evening—nothing intimate, but simply a reminder of your first meeting and a suggestion that you might possibly desire to continue the acquaintanceship. Quotations from poetry of the better sort are always appropriate; thus, on this occasion, it might be nice to write on the card accompanying the flowers—" 'This is the forest primeval'—H. W. Longfellow," or " 'Take, oh take, those lips away'—W. Shakespeare." You will find there are hundreds of lines equally appropriate for this and other occasions, and in this connection it might be well to display a little originality at times by substituting pertinent verses of your own in place of the conventional quotations. For example—"This is the forest primeval, I regret your last evening's upheaval," shows the young lady in question that not only are you well-read in classic poetry, but also you have no mean talent of your own. Too much originality, however, is dangerous, especially in polite social intercourse, and I need hardly remind you that the floors of the social ocean are watered with the tears of those who seek to walk on their own hook.

Within a week after you have sent the young lady the flowers, you should receive a polite note of thanks, somewhat as follows: "My dear Mr. Roe: Those lovely flowers came quite as a surprise. They are lovely, and I cannot thank you enough for your thoughtfulness. Their lovely fragrance fills my room as I write, and I wish to thank you again. It was lovely of you."

Flowers and Their Message in Courtship

It is now time to settle down to the more serious business of courtship. Her letter shows beyond the shadow of a figurative doubt that she is "interested," and the next move is "up to you." Probably she will soon come into the office to see her father, in which case you should have ready at hand some appropriate gift, such as, for example, a nice potted geranium. Great care should be taken, however, that it is a plant of the correct species, for in the etiquette of courtship all flowers have different meanings and many a promising affair has been ruined because a suitor sent his lady a buttercup, meaning "That's the last dance I'll ever take you to, you big cow," instead of a plant with a more tender significance. Some of the commoner flowers and their meaning in courtship are as follows:

Fringed Gentian—"I am going out to get a shave. Back at three-thirty."

Poppy—"I would be proud to be the father of your children."

Goldenrod—"I hear that you have hay fever."

Tuberose—"Meet me Saturday at the Fourteenth Street subway station."

Blood-root—"Aunt Kitty murdered Uncle Fred Thursday."

Dutchman's Breeches—"That case of Holland gin and Old Tailor has arrived. Come on over."

Iris—"Could you learn to love an optician?"

Aster—"Who was that stout Jewish-looking party I saw you with in the hotel lobby Friday?"

Deadly Nightshade—"Pull down those blinds, quick!"

Passion Flower—"Phone Main 1249—ask for Eddie."

Raspberry—"I am announcing my engagement to Charlie O'Keefe Tuesday."

Wild Thyme—"I have seats for the Hippodrome Saturday afternoon."

The above flowers can also be combined to make different meanings, as, for example, a bouquet composed of three tuberoses and some Virginia creeper generally signifies the following, "The reason I didn't call for you yesterday was that I had three inner tube punctures, besides a lot of engine trouble in that old car I bought in Virginia last year. Gosh, I'm sorry!"

But to return to the etiquette of our present courtship. As Miss Doe leaves the office you follow her, holding the potted plant in your left hand. After she has gone a few paces you step up to her, remove your hat (or cap) with your right hand, and offer her the geranium, remarking, "I beg your pardon, miss, but didn't you drop this?" A great deal depends upon the manner in which you offer the plant and the way she receives it. If you hand it to her with the flower pointing upward it means, "Dare I hope?" Reversed, it signifies, "Your petticoat shows about an inch, or an inch and a half." If she receives the plant in her right hand, it means, "I am"; left hand, "You are"; both hands—"He, she or it is." If, however, she takes the pot firmly in both hands and breaks it with great force on your head, the meaning is usually negative and your only correct course of procedure is a hasty bow and a brief apology.

Receiving an Invitation To Call

Let us suppose, however, that she accepts the geranium in such a manner that you are encouraged to continue the acquaintance. Your next move should be a request for an invitation to call upon her at her home. This should, above all things, not be done crudely. It is better merely to suggest your wish by some indirect method such as, "Oh—so you live on William Street. Well, well! I often walk on William Street in the evening, but I have never called on any girl there—

yet." The "yet" may be accompanied by a slight raising of your eyebrows, a wink, or a friendly nudge with your elbow. Unless she is unusually "dense" she will probably "take the hint" and invite you to come and see her some evening. At once you should say, *"What* evening? How about *tonight?"* If she says that she is already engaged for that evening, take a calendar out of your pocket and remark, "Tomorrow? Wednesday? Thursday? Friday? I really have no engagements between now and October. Saturday? Sunday?" This will show her that you are really desirous of calling upon her and she will probably say, "Well, I think I am free Thursday night, but you had better telephone me first."

The Etiquette of Telephoning

On Thursday morning, therefore, you should go to a public telephone-booth in order to call the young lady's house. The etiquette of telephoning is quite important and many otherwise perfectly well-bred people often make themselves conspicuous because they do not know the correct procedure in using this modern but almost indispensable invention. Upon entering the telephone-booth, which is located, say, in some drug store, you remove the receiver from the hook and deposit the requisite coin in the coin box. After an interval of some minutes a young lady (referred to as "Central") will ask for your "Number, please." Suppose, for example, that you wish to get Bryant 4310. Remove your hat politely and speak that number into the mouthpiece. "Central" will then say, "Rhinelander 4310." To which you reply, *"No,* Central—*Bryant* 4310." Central then says, "I beg your pardon—Bryant 4310," to which you reply, "Yes, please." In a few minutes a voice at the other end of the line says, "Hello," to which you answer, "Is Miss Doe at home?" The voice then says, "Who?" You say, "Miss Doe, please—Miss Dorothy Doe." You then hear the following, "Wait a minute. Say, Charlie, is they anybody works around here by the name of Doe? There's a guy wants to talk to a Miss Doe. Here—you answer it." Another voice then says, "Hello." You reply, "Hello." He says, "What do you want?" You reply, "I wish to speak to Miss Dorothy Doe." He says, "What department does she work in?" You reply, "Is this the residence of J. Franklin Doe, President of the First National Bank?" He says, "Wait a minute." You wait a minute. You wait several. Another voice—a new voice says—"Hello." You reply, "Hello." He says, "Give me Stuyvesant 8864." You say, "But I'm trying to get Miss Doe— Miss Dorothy Doe." He says, "Who?" You say, "Is this the residence of ——" He says, "Naw—this is Goebel Brothers, Wholesale Grocers—what number do you want?" You say, "Bryant 4310." He says, "Well, this is Rhinelander 4310." You then hang up the receiver and count twenty. The telephone bell then rings, and inasmuch as you are the only person near the phone you take up the receiver and say, "Hello." A female voice says, "Hello, dearie—don't you know who this is?" You say, politely but firmly, "No." She says, "Guess!" You guess "Mrs. Warren G. Harding." She says, "No. This is Ethel. Is Walter there?" You reply, "Walter?" She says, "Ask him to come to the phone, will you? He lives up-stairs over the drug store. Just yell 'Walter' at the third door down the hall. Tell him Ethel wants to speak to him—no, wait—tell him it's Madge." Being a gentleman, you comply with the lady's request. After bringing Walter to the phone, you obligingly wait for some twenty minutes while he converses with Ethel— no, Madge. When he has finished, you once more enter the booth and tell "Central" you want Bryant 4310. After a few minutes "Central" says, "What number did you call?" You say patiently, "Bryant 4310." She replies, "Bryant 4310 has been changed to Schuyler 6372." You ask for Schuyler 6372. Finally a woman's voice says, "Yass." You say, "Is Miss Doe in?" She replies, "Yass." You say, "May I speak to her?" She says, "Who?" You reply, "You said Miss Doe was at home, didn't you?" She replies, "Yass." You say, "Well, may I speak to her?" The voice says, "Who?" You shout, "Miss Doe." The voice says, "She ban out." You shriek, "Oh, go to hell!" and assuming a graceful, easy position in the booth, you proceed to tear the telephone from the wall. Later on in the day, when you have two or three hours of spare time, you can telephone Miss Doe again and arrange for the evening's visit.

Making the First Call

The custom of social "calls" between young men and young women is one of the prettiest of etiquette's older conventions, and one around which clusters a romantic group of delightful traditions. In this day and generation, what with horseless carriages, electric telephones and telegraphs, and dirigible gas bags, a great many of the older forms have been allowed to die out, greatly, I believe, to our discredit. "Speed, not manners," seems to be the motto of this century. I hope that there still exist a few young men who care enough about "good form" to study carefully to perfect themselves in the art of "calling." Come, Tom, Dick and Harry—drop your bicycles for an afternoon and fill your minds with something besides steam engines and pneumatic tires!

The first call at the home of any young lady of fashion is an extremely important social function, and too great care cannot be taken that you prepare yourself thoroughly in advance. It would be well to leave your work an hour or two earlier in the afternoon, so that you can go home and practice such necessary things as entering or leaving a room correctly. Most young men are extremely careless in this particular, and unless you rehearse yourself thoroughly in the proper procedure you are apt to find later on to your dismay that you have made your exit through a window onto the fire-escape instead of through the proper door.

Conversation and Some of Its Uses

Your conversation should also be planned more or less in advance. Select some topic in which you think your lady friend will be interested, such as, for example, the removal of tonsils and adenoids, and "read up" on the subject so that you can discuss it in an intelligent manner. Find out, for example, how many people had tonsils removed in February, March, April. Contrast this with the same figures for 1880, 1890, 1900. Learn two or three amusing anecdotes about adenoids. Consult Bartlett's "Familiar Quotations" for appropriate verses dealing with tonsils and throat troubles. Finally, and above all, take time to glance through four or five volumes of Dr. Eliot's Five Foot Shelf, for nothing so completely marks the cultivated man as the ability to refer familiarly to the various volumes of the Harvard classics.

A Proper Call

Promptly at the time appointed you should arrive at the house where the young lady is staying. In answer to your ring a German police dog will begin to bark furiously inside the house, and a maid will finally come to the door. Removing your hat and one glove, you say, "Is Miss Doe home?" The maid replies, "Yass, ay tank so." You give her your card and the dog rushes out and bites you on either the right or left leg. You are then ushered into a room in which is seated an old man with a long white beard. He is fast asleep. "Dot's grampaw," says the maid, to which you reply, "Oh." She retires, leaving you alone with grampaw. After a while he opens his eyes and stares at you for a few minutes. He then says, "Did the dog bite you?" You answer, "Yes, sir." Grampaw then says, "He bites everybody," and goes back to sleep. Reassured, you light a cigarette. A little boy and girl then come to the door, and, after examining you carefully for several minutes, they burst into giggling laughter and run away. You feel to see if you have forgotten to put on a necktie. A severe-looking old lady then enters the room. You rise and bow. "I am Miss Doe's grandmother. Someone has been smoking in here," she says, and sits down opposite you. Her remark is not, however, a hint for a cigarette and you should not make the mistake of saying, "I've only got Fatimas, but if you care to try one——" It should be your aim to seek to impress yourself favorably upon every member of the young lady's family. Try to engage the grandmother in conversation, taking care to select subjects in which you feel she would be interested. Conversation is largely the art of "playing up" to the other person's favorite subject. In this particular case, for example, it would be a mistake to say to Miss Doe's grandmother, "Have you ever tried making synthetic gin?" or "Do you think anyone will *ever* lick Dempsey?" A more experienced person, and someone who had studied the hobbies of old people, would probably begin by remarking, "Well, I see that Jeremiah Smith died of cancer Thursday," or "That was a lovely burial they gave Mrs. Watts, wasn't it?" If you are tactful, you should soon win the old lady's favor completely, so that before long she will tell you all about her rheumatism and what grampaw can and can't eat.

Finally Miss Doe arrives. Her first words are, "Have you been waiting long? Hilda didn't tell me you were here," to which you reply, "No—I just arrived." She then says, "Shall we go in the drawing-room?" The answer to this is, "For God's sake, yes!" In a few minutes you find yourself alone in the drawing-room with the lady of your choice and the court-ship proper can then begin.

The best way to proceed is gradually to bring the con-versation around to the subject of the "modern girl." After your preliminary remarks about tonsils and adenoids have been thoroughly exhausted, you should suddenly say, "Well, I don't think girls—nice girls—are really that way." She replies, of course, "*What* way?" You answer, "Oh, the way they are in these modern novels. This 'petting,' for instance." She says, "*What 'petting'?*" You walk over and sit down on the sofa beside her. "Oh," you say, "these novelists make me sick— they seem to think that in our generation every time a young man and woman are left alone on a lounge together, they haven't a thing better to do than put out the light and 'pet.' It's disgusting, isn't it?" "Isn't it?" she agrees and reaching over she accidentally pulls the lamp cord, which puts out the light.

On your first visit you should not stay after 12:30.

The Proposal Proper

About the second or third month of a formal courtship it is customary for the man to propose matrimony, and if the girl has been "out" for three or four years and has several younger sisters coming along, it is customary for her to accept him. They then become "engaged," and the courtship is concluded.

DONALD OGDEN STEWART was born in 1894 in Columbus, Ohio. He graduated from Exeter and Yale, where he learned his etiquette. During World War I he served in the U.S. Navy. His first book, *A Parody Outline of History,* was published when he was twenty-seven years old.

In 1928, convinced that his six-foot frame and rimless spectacles would make him irresistible to the theater-going public, he took up acting. Two years later he moved to Hollywood to work as a screenwriter. He wrote and collaborated on many screenplays, including the classics *Dinner at Eight, The Prisoner of Zenda,* and *Life with Father.* He won an Oscar for his work on *The Philadelphia Story.*

Mr. Stewart, who is always represented in collections of humor, has written many books—too numerous to list here. They are all funny, and some are also suitable for pressing flowers or other mementos.

STEVE ALLEN

The Late-Show Pitchman

One of Allen's TV classics of the early fifties was a takeoff on an advertising spiel that in those days was all over everybody's TV screen—seemingly almost twenty-four hours a day—the Charles Antell commercial. Its announcers were pitchmen of the old-fashioned sidewalk or dime-store type, and Allen was fascinated by their fast-talking, almost hypnotic style. In delivering the following monologue he copied the high-pressure pitchman manner with such success that to this day the TV pitchman is one of his regular TV characters.

Although Allen conceived and wrote much of the Antell takeoff himself, he wishes it known that significant contributions to it were made by Bill Larkin and Larry Markes, writers then on his staff.

Ladies and Gennemum, make yourselves comfortable and turn up the volume, because I'm going to tell you a big hair-raising story. And when I say BIG I mean BIG, and when I say STORY I mean STORY. Because I am one of the biggest story tellers on the air today!

And correct me if I'm wrong.

For instance, did you know that there are over 500,000 bald women in this country and over ten million bald *men?* The reason you don't notice the bald women is you think they're bald men.

But see my hair? These roots are not dead! Men, are you bald? Does your head keep slipping off the pillow at night?

Do you know what makes you bald? I'll *tell* you what makes you bald. Not having any *hair* makes you bald!

Know what *else* makes you bald? *Worry.* Know what you worry about? Losing your hair!

If you have trouble with your hair, let us get rid of it for you!

When a man starts to lose his hair he usually goes to a baldheaded barber and asks him what he should do. So the barber gets a little perfumed alcohol and sprinkles it on the guy's head. If alcohol could grow hair, most of the men I know would choke to death. *Don't* let the barber pour alcohol on your head! Put it where it'll do the most good. *Drink* it and let it get at the roots of your hair from the *inside.* And let the barber shave your tonsils!

A wonderful exercise is to grab your hair and pull it. Women have better hair than men because the longer hair pulls and strengthens the follicles. Make this interesting test tonight when you get home. Grab your wife's hair and give it a good hard yank. Pull her right off the ground and then let her trickle slowly through your fingers. Now grab *your* hair and pull it. Notice how it burns and irritates as it tears out?

Look at your scalp. Is it dry and parched? Now compare your scalp with your neighbor's scalp. For this interesting hobby of collecting and comparing scalps, send for our special Indian knife, with the sharpest edges ever honed.

What do you *ladies* do to your hair? I'll tell you what you do, and correct me if I'm wrong! You dye it, fry it, curl it, swirl it, roast it, toast it, spin it, pin it, oil it, boil it, stuff it, puff it, mash it, smash it, hack it, shellac it, scent it, cement it. You cut it poodle, noodle, apple strudel, every way but Yankee Doodle. You pinch it with pins, and stuff it with cotton, good times there are not forgotten, look away, look away, Dixieland! I wish I was in Dixie! (Pardon me friends, I got carried away.)

As I was saying, ladies, your hair is drenched, wrenched, torched, scorched, incinerated, and embalmed. They take the vitamins and minerals from your hair, they put it in feed for your hogs and cattle. And that's why the pigs that your farmers raise are healthy and win blue ribbons, and the children the farmers raise are rheumatic, diabetic, nervous, and baldheaded!

Scientists have discovered why the women of southern Italy have such wavy hair. You know the reason? Because all through their early years they carry wicker baskets on their heads.

Lots of girls give themselves a home permanent. So they run down to the drugstore and buy themselves a chemistry set. And after they've given themselves a home permanent, they *have* to stay home. Permanent.

This won't happen if you use Charley's Aunt's Formula. Did you know that sheep are the only animals that have to get haircuts? (Next time you're counting sheep notice their hair. You have *never* seen a bald sheep!) The reason is obvious. The sheep use our product. Friends, this formula will grow hair on a billiard ball, if you don't mind playing pool with hairy billiard balls.

Now I'd like to make a little experiment. Here are three ordinary pieces of writing paper and a bowl of water. I place nothing on the first sheet and dip it into the water. What happens? The paper gets sopping wet. On the second sheet, I place a little mineral oil. And when I dip it in the water, the water runs off, and the mineral oil leaves the paper stained. But, on the *third* piece of paper, I place a little lanolin, and when I dip it in the water the paper rolls up into a tight curl. This proves conclusively that if you want curly writing paper, fill your pen with lanolin!

The same thing happens to sheep on a damp day. There is a natural curl that no amount of pulling or tugging can take out. Ladies, if you want to be seen with curly hair, go out on rainy days with sheep.

Now you saw me put Charley's Aunt on my hair four times during the course of my lecture. I give six or seven lectures a day, six days a week, and I wash my hair two or three times a year. Can you imagine how dirty my hair would be if I didn't have my head drained and the oil changed every thousand miles?

Now watch. Merely by running a damp cloth through my hair the waves fall right into place, each one just a little *tighter* than it was before. The same thing happens when it rains. I get tight.

Charley's Aunt's Formula Number 9 contains no harmful ingredients. It does not contain sulphur, or cyanide, or Serutan. It does not contain harsh abrasives, smooth abrasives, latakia, apple honey, irrium, solium, birdseed, nitrates, or day rates. Charley's Aunt contains *lanolin,* the only sheep oil that contains chicken fat! This lanolin is obtained from the backs of happy lambs. They get them happy by feeding them pure grain alcohol, and when the sheep are well oiled, they drain them.

Here's a letter from a satisfied user. She used to be completely bald. Now she has beautiful red hair all the way down her back. Too bad it didn't grow on her head.

Well, you can have a beautiful hair too. And under our sensational offer, you can't lose. You call us at these numbers . . . and a bottle of Charley's Aunt will be sent to you C.O.D. You pay the postman and *he* gives you the shampoo.

And as a special offer, a large, economy-size bottle of our special shampoo, which contains Drano. You put it on and rinse it off four times. It doesn't keep your hair from falling out, but it's awful clean when it hits the floor. Try our amazing thirty-day trial. If you don't bring us to trial in thirty days, we'll be amazed. The price? One can for five bucks, two cans for ten bucks, and our special offer, *five* cans for *ten* bucks.

After using Charley's Aunt's Formula Number 9, ask yourself, "Do I look better?" If your answer is, "WHAAAT, look better?" this offer won't cost you one red cent, because they don't make that color any more.

And now, back to our feature, "The Bowery Boys Meet the Dead End Kids."

STEVE ALLEN has been ad-libbing his way into the hearts of the public for more than twenty years. He headed several of the first funny interview shows on radio and television, and was one of the first entertainers to keep sleepy America glued to its television sets after midnight.

He was born in New York City in 1921. Both his parents were vaudeville performers. In their act, Steve Allen's mother was the comic and his father was the straight man. Because his parents played vaudeville houses all over the country, Steve Allen attended sixteen different schools and colleges. After attending journalism school in Iowa and Arizona, he was hired by a Phoenix radio station, where he worked as an announcer, piano player, and writer of commercials. Later, in Los Angeles, he was a comedian on a show called *Smile Time* and an announcer for wrestling matches. In 1947 CBS signed him as a radio disk jockey. But before CBS knew what was happening, the show had changed from a music program to a comedy program, with Mr. Allen interviewing members of the audience and cracking jokes.

In 1950 *The Steve Allen Show* became a national television program. Its formula for success has been imitated by many other programs since then. The formula was simple enough. Mr. Allen interviewed guests, or if the guests were boring he took his cameras out into the streets and interviewed bewildered passers-by. He read letters from the audience, played the piano, or simply talked about what was on his mind. He now has a similar television show seen in the New York area.

Mr. Allen plays the piano quite well, and has composed about two thousand songs. Once, on a bet, he wrote fifty songs per day for a week. He has also appeared in a Broadway play and in several movies. He is married to the actress Jayne Meadows. His books include *The Funnymen* and an account of his radio and TV career, *Bigger Than a Breadbox*.

RICHARD ARMOUR

The Discovery of America

America was founded by Columbus in 1492. This is an easy date to remember because it rhymes with "ocean blue," which was the color of the Atlantic in those days. If he had sailed a year later the date would still be easy to remember because it would rhyme with "boundless sea."

Columbus fled to this country because of persecution by Ferdinand and Isabella, who refused to believe the world was round, even when Columbus showed them an egg. Ferdinand later became famous because he objected to bullfights and said he preferred to smell flowers if he had to smell anything. He was stung in the end by a bee.

Before Columbus reached America, which he named

after a man called American Vesuvius, he cried "Ceylon! Ceylon!" because he wanted to see India, which was engraved on his heart, before he died. When he arrived, he cried again. This time he cried "Excelsior!" meaning "I have founded it." Excelsior has been widely used ever since by persons returning with chinaware from China, with indiaware from India, and with underware from Down Under.

Columbus was mistaken in thinking he had reached India when actually he had not got even as far as Indiana. There is still a great deal of confusion about the East and the West. As Columbus discovered, if you go west long enough you find yourself in the east, and vice versa. The East and the West are kept apart by the Date Line, just as the North and South are kept apart by the Masons' Dixon Line. In the New World most of the eastern half of the country is called the Middle West, although it is known as the East by those who live in the Far West.

Columbus, who was as confused as anybody who has been at sea for a long time, called the first people he saw "Indians." It is not known what they called Columbus. His unfortunate error has been perpetuated through the centuries. The original Americans are still known as "Indians," while all manner of immigrants from England, Ireland, Angora, and Liechtenstein are referred to as "Americans."[1]

Accompanied by his devoted followers, the Knights of Columbus, Columbus made several other voyages in search of India. Try as he might, however, he kept discovering America, and finally returned to Spain to die. He lived for a time in Madrid, but spent his last days in Disgrace.

[1] Or, by their mathematically inclined friends, "100 percent Americans."

A Minority Opinion

Some say it was not Columbus who discovered America but a man named Leaf Ericson. Leaf came from one of the Scandinavian countries with a shipload of people, all of whom were called Yon Yonson or Ole Olson or Big Swede, and went straight to Wisconsin, where he unloaded his passengers and went back for more.

On his next trip he went to Minnesota.

We know all this from some undecipherable remarks he made on a piece of stone. This stone has since become an utter rune.

Further Explorations

After Columbus proved the world was round, a great many people went around it. Marco Polo, who was one of the earlier explorers, had the misfortune to live several centuries before Columbus. Therefore, although he got around a good deal, he did not get completely around. He went far to the north, however, and is remembered for his discovery of the Polo regions.

The chief rivals in exploration were England and Spain. England had men like Cabot, who spoke only to a man named Lowell, and Sir Francis Drake, who had a singed beard and a ship called the *Golden Behind*.

Nor should we forget Sir Martin Fourflusher.[2]

The struggle between England and Spain came to a

---

[2] A direct descendant of the early Saxons, who knew all the Angles.

climax in an epic sea battle off the Azores known as the Last Fight of the Revenge. In this decisive conflict, Sir Richard Grenville and Alfred Lord Tennyson proved conclusively that the lighter English warships could get more miles to the galleon.

England has ruled the waves ever since and has kept the sun from setting anywhere on her empire, thus providing a longer working day than in other countries.

Still Further Explorations

Other explorers included Bilbo, Cabbage de Vaca, Cortez (known as The Stout, who traveled much in realms looking for gold), and Pantsy de Lion, a thirsty old man who was looking for a drinking fountain.[3] He never found it, but he founded Florida, to which a great many thirsty old men have gone ever since.

THE VIRGINIA COLONY

All this time there was not much happening in the New World, except that it was steadily growing older.

This period, known as the Doldrums, came to an end in fifteen-something-or-other when Sir Walter Raleigh, a man with a pointed beard and a pointless way of muddying his cloak, established a colony in America in the hope of pleasing the Queen, whose favor he had been in but was temporarily out of.

---

[3] Some historians say that in his wanderings through the South he invented the Dixie cup, just in case.

Although he claimed the new land in the name of Elizabeth, he called it Virginia, which aroused suspicions in Elizabeth's mind and caused her to confine Sir Walter in a tower. While imprisoned, Sir Walter made good use of his time by writing a history of the world on such scraps of paper as he could find, and filling other scraps of paper with a weed brought back from Virginia.

He had barely completed his history when he lost his head. Had he been permitted to keep it a few years longer he might have become the first man to roll a cigarette with one hand.

The Virginia Colony was lost for a time, and its name was changed to The Lost Colony, but it was subsequently found at about the place where it was last seen. Its original name of Virginia was restored because Elizabeth no longer cared, being dead.[4]

The Indians

The people who were already in the New World when the white men arrived were the first Americans, or America Firsters. They were also referred to as the First Families of Virginia.

The early colonists found the Indians living in toupees, or wigwams, and sending up smoke signals, or wigwags, with piece pipes. Apparently because of a shortage of pipes, they sat in a circle and passed one pipe around, each biting off a piece as it passed. The chief Indian was named Hiawatha, and his squaw, whose name was Evangeline, did all the work. This was later to become an Old American Custom.

[4] The end of Elizabeth is known as the Elizabethan Period.

The Chiefs, it must be said in all fairness, were too busy to work. They were engaged in making wampum, or whoopee, when they were not mixing war paint or scattering arrowheads about, to be found centuries later.

In order to have their hands free to work, the squaws carried their babies, or cabooses, on their back, very much as kangaroos carry their babies on their front, only different.

The Indians were stern, silent people who never showed their feelings, even while being scalped. They crept up on their enemies without breaking a twig and were familiar with all the warpaths. Despite their savage ways, they sincerely loved peace, and were called Nobel Savages.

Their favorite word was "How," which the colonists soon learned was not a question.

The whites feared the redskins and considered them the forest's prime evil. Some went so far as to say that "The only good Indian is a wooden Indian." The redskins resented the whiteskins because they thought they had come to take their lands away from them, and their fears were well grounded.

Captain John Smith

Captain John Smith was the first of a long line of Smiths who came to this country to keep up with the Joneses.

He was captured by the great Indian Chief, Powhatan, and was about to be killed when Popocatepetl, the fiery young daughter of the Chief, stepped in. We are not told what she stepped in, but she saved Captain John Smith's life, for which he thanked her. Later she married an Englishman, which improved relations.

THE PILGRIMS

The Pilgrims were a branch of the Puritans, and were proud of their family tree.[5] They wore tall hats, which they had to take off when they went inside because they attended a low church. This displeased King James, who raised the roof. He demanded that they attend the same church as he did. At least this is his side of the story, which became known as the King James Version.

Although the King insisted, the Puritans, who were very stiff-necked from years of wearing truffles on their collars, stubbornly declined. They would probably still be declining if they had not left England and gone to Leyden, a city in Holland noted for the discovery of electricity in a jar. (Electricity was subsequently lost for a while, but was rediscovered, by accident, when Benjamin Franklin was told to go fly a kite, and did.)

While in Holland, the Pilgrims suffered from pangs of sin,[6] and sent their children to Dutch Reform Schools when they misbehaved. These children, naturally enough, became Protestants, but their protests were ignored.

The Plymouth Colony

After several years in Holland, the Pilgrims decided to set out for the New World. This decision to move is known as Pilgrims' Progress.

[5] These, it should be noted, were the first Puritans. The last Puritan was a Spanish nun named Santa Anna.

[6] Some years later a man named Sigmund Fraud claimed they enjoyed it.

The ship on which they sailed was the *Mayflower*. In stormy weather the women and children descended below the heaving decks, thus becoming the *Mayflower* descendants. There they huddled with the Colonial Dames and other early settlers and passed the weary hours comparing genealogies.

It was a long and perilous voyage across the Atlantic. Several times they were blown off their course. But finally, in 1620, which was a doubly Memorable Year because it was also the year in which they set sail, they sighted the rocky coast. The rock on which they landed they called Plymouth Rock because it reminded them of another rock of the same name in England. They built a small picket fence around it and made it a national shrine.

The first four men ashore became our fourfathers.

The First Winter

After a short stay on Plymouth Rock, which was windy and damp, the Pilgrims sought a more sheltered place to build a town. One party went in one direction and one went in another. This was the beginning of the two-party system. When the two parties met, they held the first town meeting.

The first winter was cold,[7] which was a distinct surprise to the Pilgrims. Indeed, they might not have survived but for the corn that was given them by friendly Indians. By a curious quirk of history, it has since become illegal for white men to give Indians either corn or rye.

One thing that helped the Pilgrims get through the winter was the economical practice of putting young men

[7] Probably responsible for the blue noses which became one of the Pilgrims' outstanding features.

and women into bed together, fully clothed. This odd practice, known as bungling, was endured by the young people of the colony until the weather became milder and a sufficient supply of bed-warmers could be imported from England.

The next spring the crops were good, and in the fall the Pilgrims celebrated their first Thanksgiving, which fell, that fall, on a Thursday. The friendly Indians were invited, and the unfriendly Indians stayed in the background, muttering.

Captain Miles Standish

One of the leaders of the little band[8] at Plymouth was Captain Miles Standish. He was known throughout the township for his courtship.

He was an exceptional man. Except for him, almost all the Pilgrims were named William or John. One of the latter was Miles Standish's friend, quiet John Alden, a man who did not speak for himself until spoken to. He was spoken to, and sharply, by the fair Priscilla, whom he married, much to the annoyance of Miles Standish, who thought he was stood up by his stand-in.

THE COLONIES GROW

Let us leave the Pilgrims in Plymouth and see what was happening elsewhere in New England.

Education took a forward step with the founding of Harvard in a yard near the Charles River. Among the early

---

8 A precursor of such bandleaders as Paul Whiteman and Benny Goodman.

benefactors of Harvard was a plantation owner from the South known as "Cotton" Mather. The first library was only a five-foot shelf, given to the college by T. S. Eliot, a graduate who no longer had need of it.[9] The books on this shelf are known as the Great Books and have grown to one hundred.

With the founding of two other old colleges, Old Eli and Old Nassau, the educational system was complete. Because of the ivory towers which were a distinctive feature of many of the early buildings, the three colleges became known as the Ivory League.

To provide recreational facilities for students at Harvard, the city of Boston was established. Boston became famous for its two famous hills, Beacon and Bunker, its two famous churches, North and South, and its two famous bays, Back and Front.

The people of Boston became wealthy by exporting baked beans and codfish, which they were smart enough not to eat themselves. Many, who were pillars of the church and pillars of society, came to be known as Propper Bostonians.

Williams and Penn

One who was unhappy with life in Plymouth was Roger Williams, who thought the Pilgrims were intolerable. The Pilgrims, in turn, thought Williams was impossible. He proposed that they pay the Indians for their land instead of simply taking it from them. This utopian suggestion was dismissed by the Pilgrims as economically unsound.

Because of his unorthodox views, the Pilgrims branded him. They branded him a heretic, and drove him from town

---

[9] Having made a fortune in real estate by the sale of wasteland.

to town, although he preferred to walk. This was why Roger Williams reluctantly left Plymouth and founded Rhode Island, which is really not an island and is so small that it is usually indicated on maps by the letters "R.I." out in the Atlantic Ocean. It was once densely wooded. It is now densely populated.[10]

William Penn, on the other hand, came to America to collect some land the King owed his father. He belonged to a frightened religious sect known as the Quakers. So that he would not be forgotten, he gave his name to the Pennsylvania Railroad, the Pennsylvania Station, and the state prison, which is known as the Penn.

Massachusetts Bay

The English had always been a seafaring race, ever since they were Danes. Therefore one of their first acts in the New World was to make Massachusetts Bay a colony. From Massachusetts Bay and the nearby bayous they went out in their high-masted vessels looking for whale oil, which they found mostly in whales. The men who went away on voyages to capture whales were called whalers. So, by coincidence, were their sturdy ships. This is more confusing to us now than it was then.

The most famous whale, in those days, was an ill-tempered, unpredictable old whale called Moody Dick. Everyone was on the lookout for him, especially whalers whose legs he had bitten off in one of his nastier moods. The one-legged whaler who was most resentful was Captain A. Hab, who persisted until he finally managed to harpoon Moody Dick

---

[10] Many, with leftist political leanings, became Rhode Island Reds.

where it hurt the most. The whale had the last word, however, for he overturned Captain A. Hab's ship, the *Peapod*, which went down with all hands, including both of Captain A. Hab's.

Connecticut

Fortunately for those who liked to visit New York but preferred not to live there, Connecticut was founded within commuting distance.

It was founded by Thomas Hooker, a clergyman who, in a dim church, interpreted the Gospel according to his own lights. He would also accept no money for his preaching, which set a low wage standard for others; he was therefore scorned as a free thinker. So he left under a cloud. Many of his parishioners believed his stern words about hell and followed him to Hartford, where he guaranteed them protection in the hereafter and sold them the first fire-insurance policies.

Connecticut is usually spelled Conn, which is easier.

LIFE IN OLD NEW ENGLAND

Most of the Puritans were ministers. Each week they could hardly wait until Sunday, when they preached for several hours on such subjects as "Hellfire" and "Damnation." In those days, church attendance was as good every Sunday as it is today on Easter.

All the Puritans, except a few who should never have left England, were opposed to sin. When a woman sinned, they pinned a scarlet letter "A" on her breast, where it would be conspicuous. Women who won their letter year after year were disdainfully called Scarlet, like Scarlet O'Hara and Scarlet Pimpernel. Children were kept in innocence of the meaning of the "A" and thought it stood for "Adulthood," when such things usually happened.

The homes of the Puritans were simple and austere, but their furniture was antique and therefore frightfully expensive. The chairs were as straight and stiff as the Puritans themselves, and had hard bottoms. They became known as period pieces because they went to pieces after a short period of sitting on them. The women had large chests or collector's items, of which they were extremely proud. Some of these have been handed down from generation to generation and are displayed proudly by their owners today.

Stores were known as Shoppes, or Ye Olde Shoppes. Prices were somewhat higher at the latter.

The Puritans believed in justice. A woman who was a witch, or a man who was a son of a witch, was punished by being stuck in the stocks. These were wooden devices that had holes to put the arms and legs through, and were considered disgraceful. They were also considered uncomfortable.

Every day the men went out into the fields in their blunderbusses and sowed corn. The women, meanwhile, were busy at home embroidering the alphabet and the date on a piece of cloth. One of the women, Hester Primmer, one of the New England Primmers, never got beyond the first letter of the alphabet. She also had only one date. That was with a young minister and was enough.

Other amusements were pillories, whipping posts, and Indian massacres.

The Land

The land was stony and hilly, except in places where it was hilly and stony. The stones were useful for making millstones and milestones. The Indians sharpened them and used them for scalping and other social purposes.

The hills were useful to watch for Indians from, unless the Indians were already on them. They were hard to plow up, but they were relatively easy to plow down.

The Climate

The winters in New England were long. Largely for this reason, the summers were short. In keeping with the seasons, long underwear was worn in the winter and short underwear in the summer.

THE DUTCH AND THE FRENCH COME TO AMERICA

Many believed there was a shorter way to get to Asia than around America. Not yet having discovered the Panama Canal, they were looking for the next best thing, which was the Northwest Passage. Since it did not exist, it was, of course, hard to find. Nevertheless many Intrepid Explorers made their reputation hunting for it.

One of those who sought the Northwest Passage was Henry Hudson. In a ship of which he was part owner, called the *Half Mine,* he led a crew of Dutchmen to the mouth of the Hudson River, which he was pleased to find named after himself.

Stopping only to make friends with the Indians and to buy the island of Manhattan from an Indian named Minnehaha (or "Laughing Minnie") for a handful of beads,[11] he pushed on up the river. When he stopped pushing he was in Albany, and he was disappointed. The water was getting shallower and shallower and it was clear. It was clear that this was not the Northwest Passage, and that instead of founding an important route to the Orient, he was about to founder at the state capital. The choice was also clear. He must remain in Albany or make the hard and perilous voyage back across the Atlantic. Without hesitation he chose the latter.

On a second trip to the New World in search of the elusive Passage, Henry Hudson sailed into Hudson Bay. This, again, was not the Northwest Passage, but its name had a familiar ring.

It is not known what became of this Able Navigator who had not been able to find what he was looking for. One theory is that Hudson met Cadillac and De Soto, and that together they discovered Detroit.

New Amsterdam

Because of Henry Hudson's explorations, the Dutch laid claim to the mouth of the Hudson River, which in their systematic way they divided into the North River and the East River. A stubborn race, they named Manhattan New Amsterdam, although it was obviously New York.

---

[11] Beads were then selling at $24 a handful.

New Amsterdam was soon swarming with wealthy Dutch traitors known as poltroons. These were bluff, hearty men who smoked long pipes and loved to eat burghers. They frequently had their pictures painted, and one of the most picturesque was their Governor, Rip Van Wrinkle, a one-legged gentleman who fell into a deep sleep while watching a bowling game.

The English also claimed Manhattan, in view of the fact that the beads with which it was purchased were plainly stamped "Made in England." The Dutch could not see the merits of their claim, but they could see that the English had more guns on their warships, so they left.

This was a turning point.

The clever English changed the name Amsterdam to York, but they retained the New.[12]

La Salle

The French, although exhausted by the Hundred Years' War, were not too tired to try to establish themselves in the New World. There were still mountains which had not been planted with flags, and there were still rivers that had not been sailed up. So they sailed up them. Many of these still rivers ran deep and led into fastnesses where no white man had ever trod and very few had walked.

At last the only river remaining to be sailed up was the Mississippi. In this instance the French explorer La Salle defied convention. A headstrong young man, he began at the headwaters of the mighty river and sailed down it. He thus

---

[12] The city was later called New York, New York, for the sake of those who did not catch it the first time.

not only opened up a vast new territory but discovered an easier means of navigating the rivers of America. La Salle's interesting account of his trip down the river, called *Life on the Mississippi,* is available in an English translation by Mark Twain.

Thanks to La Salle, the Mississippi basin remained in French hands until they grew tired of holding it and sold it for $15,000,000, which many thought was a high price for a second-hand basin.

It is to the French also that we owe the establishment of the beautiful city of Quebec, which was named, according to custom, after the King of France, whose name, according to custom, was Louis (pronounced kwĕ-bĕk'). The English later seized Quebec and its outskirts, called Canada, from the French, but not without a struggle.

Henceforth the French were dominated by the English, who became our Good Neighbors to the north. We have had amicable relations ever since by agreeing that there are two sides to everything, for example Niagara Falls, which has an American side and a Canadian side.

FIRST TEST

1. Why do you think Columbus was so interested in traveling to distant places? What else do you know about his home life?

2. Are you really convinced that the world is round? Do you worry much about it?

3. To what extent would the course of American history have been altered if America had never been discovered?

4. What would you say about the Puritans? Would you say the same if they were listening?

5. Can the passengers on the *Mayflower* be considered immigrants? With their strong sense of duty, do you suppose they tried to conceal anything from the customs officials?

6. Have you ever thought how much of a Pilgrim was wasted when an Indian kept only his scalp?

7. Trace on a map the voyages of Henry Hudson. Use a solid line to show where he went and a dotted line to show where he thought he was going. Sign on the dotted line.

8. What would you have done if you had been in La Salle's shoes? How do you know he wore any?

RICHARD ARMOUR, unlikely as it may seem, is a college professor. He was born in San Pedro, California, in 1906. He attended school there, and then went east to Harvard, where he earned his M.A. and Ph.D. degrees (clearly not worth the paper they're written on). After that, he taught at the University of Texas, Northwestern, and other colleges. During World War II he served in the army and now holds the rank of colonel in the U.S. Army Reserve. In 1945 he became professor of English at Scripps College and Claremont Graduate School in Claremont, California.

Generations of fact-hungry readers have been misinformed by Professor Armour's many books on history and literature. These include *Twisted Tales from Shakespeare, It All Started with Columbus,* and *It All Started with Europa.* He has also contributed thousands of pieces of light verse to the *Saturday Evening Post, The New Yorker,* and other magazines.

DON MARQUIS

The Case of Doc Green

From *The Rivercliff Golf Killings*

OR WHY PROFESSOR WADDEMS NEVER BROKE A HUNDRED

I am telling this story to the public just as I told it in the grand jury room; the district attorney having given me a carbon copy of my sworn testimony.

QUESTION: Professor Waddems, when did you first notice that Dr. Green seemed to harbor animosity towards you?

ANSWER: It was when we got to the second hole.

QUESTION: Professor, you may go ahead and tell the jury about it in your own words.

ANSWER: Yes, sir. The situation was this: My third shot lay in the sand in the shallow bunker—an easy pitch with a niblick to within a foot or two of the pin, for anyone who understands the theory of niblick play as well as I do. I had the hole in five, practically.

"Professor," said Doc Green, with whom I was playing—

QUESTION: This was Dr. James T. Green, the eminent surgeon, was it not?

ANSWER: Yes, sir. Dr. Green, with whom I was playing, remarked, "You are all wrong about Freud. Psychoanalysis is the greatest discovery of the age."

"Nonsense! Nonsense! Nonsense!" I replied. "Don't be a fool, Doc! I'll show you where Freud is all wrong, in a minute."

And I lifted the ball with an explosion shot to a spot eighteen inches from the pin, and holed out with an easy putt.

"Five," I said and marked it on my card.

"You mean eight," said Doc Green.

"Three into the bunker, four onto the green, and one putt—five," I said.

"You took four strokes in the bunker, Professor," he said. "Every time you said 'Nonsense' you made a swipe at the ball with your niblick."

"Great Godfrey," I said, "you don't mean to say you are going to count those gestures I made to illustrate my argument as *golf strokes?* Just mere gestures! And you know very well I have never delivered a lecture in twenty-five years without gestures like that!"

"You moved your ball an inch or two with your club at every gesture," he said.

QUESTION: Had you really done so, Professor? Remember, you are on oath.

ANSWER: I do not remember. In any case, the point is immaterial. They were merely gestures.

QUESTION: Did you take an eight, or insist on a five?

ANSWER: I took an eight. I gave in. Gentlemen, I am a good-natured person. Too good-natured. Calm and philosophical; unruffled and patient. My philosophy never leaves me. I took an eight.

(Sensation in the grand jury room.)

QUESTION: Will you tell something of your past life, Professor Waddems—who you are and what your lifework has been, and how you acquired the calmness you speak of?

ANSWER: For nearly twenty-five years I lectured on philosophy and psychology in various universities. Since I retired and took up golf it has been my habit to look at all the events and tendencies in the world's news from the standpoint of the philosopher.

QUESTION: Has this helped you in your golf?

ANSWER: Yes, sir. My philosophical and logical training and my specialization in psychology, combined with my natural calmness and patience, have made me the great golfer that I really am.

QUESTION: Have you ever received a square deal, Professor, throughout any eighteen holes of golf?

ANSWER: No, sir. Not once! Not once during the five years since I took the game up at the Rivercliff Country Club.

QUESTION: Have you ever broken a hundred, Professor Waddems?

ANSWER: No, sir. I would have, again and again, except that my opponents, and other persons playing matches on the course, and the very forces of nature themselves are always against me at critical moments. Even the bullfrogs at the three water holes treat me impertinently.

QUESTION: Bullfrogs? You said the bullfrogs, Professor?

ANSWER: Yes, sir. They have been trained by the caddies to treat me impertinently.

QUESTION: What sort of treatment have you received in the locker room?

ANSWER: The worst possible. In the case under consideration, I may say that I took an eight on the second hole, instead of insisting on a five, because I knew the sort of thing Dr. Green would say in the locker room after the match—I knew the scene he would make, and what the comments of my so-called friends would be. Whenever I do get down to a hundred an attempt is made to discredit me in the locker room.

QUESTION: Well, you took an eight on the second hole. What happened at the third hole?

ANSWER: Well, sir, I teed up for my drive, and just as I did so, Doc Green made a slighting remark about the League of Nations. "I think it is a good thing we kept out of it," he said.

QUESTION: What were your reactions?

ANSWER: A person of intelligence could only have one kind of reaction, sir. The remark was silly, narrow-minded, provincial, boneheaded, crass and ignorant. It was all the more criminal because Dr. Green knew quite well what I think of the League of Nations. The League of Nations was my idea. I thought about it even before the late President Wilson did, and talked about it and wrote about it and lectured about it in the university.

QUESTION: So that you consider Dr. Green's motives in mentioning it when you were about to drive——

ANSWER: The worst possible, sir. They could only come from a black heart at such a time.

QUESTION: Did you lost your temper, Professor?

ANSWER: No, sir! No, sir! No, sir! I *never* lose my temper! Not on any provocation. I said to myself, Be calm! Be philosophical! He's trying to get me excited! Remember what he'll say in the locker room afterwards! Be calm! Show him, show him, show him! Show him he can't get my goat.

QUESTION: Then you drove?

ANSWER: I addressed the ball the second time, sir. And I was about to drive when he said, with a sneer, "You must excuse me, Professor. I forgot that you invented the League of Nations."

QUESTION: Did you become violent, then, Professor?

ANSWER: No, sir! No, sir! I never become violent! I never——

QUESTION: Can you moderate your voice somewhat, Professor?

ANSWER: Yes, sir. I was explaining that I never become violent. I had every right to become violent. Any person less calm and philosophical would have become violent. Doc Green to criticize the League of Nations! The ass! Absurd! Preposterous! Silly! Abhorrent! Criminal! What the world wants is peace! Philosophic calm! The fool! Couldn't he understand that!

QUESTION: Aren't you departing, Professor, from the events of the 29th of last September at the Rivercliff golf course? What did you do next?

ANSWER: I drove.

QUESTION: Successfully?

ANSWER: It was a good drive, but the wind caught it, and it went out of bounds.

QUESTION: What did Dr. Green do then?

ANSWER: He grinned. A crass bonehead capable of sneering at the progress of the human race would sneer at a time like that.

QUESTION: But you kept your temper?

ANSWER: All my years of training as a philosopher came to my aid.

QUESTION: Go on, Professor.

ANSWER: I took my midiron from my bag and looked at it.

QUESTION: Well, go on, Professor. What did you think when you looked at it?

ANSWER: I do not remember, sir.

QUESTION: Come, come, Professor! You are under oath, you know. Did you think what a dent it would make in his skull?

ANSWER: Yes, sir. I remember now. I remember wondering if it would not do his brain good to be shaken up a little.

QUESTION: Did you strike him, then?

ANSWER: No, sir. I knew what they'd say in the locker room. They'd say that I lost my temper over a mere game. They would not understand that I had been jarring up his brain for his own good, in the hope of making him understand about the League of Nations. They'd say I was irritated. I know the things people always say.

QUESTION: Was there no other motive for not hitting him?

ANSWER: I don't remember.

QUESTION: Professor Waddems, again I call your attention to the fact that you are under oath. What was your other motive?

ANSWER: Oh yes, now I recall it. I reflected that if I hit him they might make me add another stroke to my score. People are always getting up the flimsiest excuses to make me add another stroke. And then accusing me of impatience if I do not acquiesce in their unfairness. I am never impatient or irritable!

QUESTION: Did you ever break a club on the course, Professor?

ANSWER: I don't remember.

QUESTION: Did you not break a mashie on the Rivercliff course last week, Professor Waddems? Reflect before you answer.

ANSWER: I either gave it away or broke it, I don't remember which.

QUESTION: Come, come, don't you remember that you broke it against a tree?

ANSWER: Oh, I think I know what you mean. But it was not through temper or irritation.

QUESTION: Tell the jury about it.

ANSWER: Well, gentlemen, I had a mashie that had a loose head on it, and I don't know how it got into my bag. My ball lay behind a sapling, and I tried to play it out from behind the tree and missed it entirely. And then I noticed I had this old mashie, which should have been gotten rid of long ago. The club had never been any good. The blade was laid back at the wrong angle. I decided that the time had come to get rid of it once and for all. So I hit it a little tap against the tree, and the head fell off. I threw the pieces over into the bushes.

QUESTION: Did you swear, Professor?

ANSWER: I don't remember. But the injustice of this incident was that my opponent insisted on counting it as a stroke and adding it to my score—my judicial, deliberate destruction of this old mashie. I never get a square deal.

QUESTION: Return to Dr. James T. Green, Professor. You are now at the third hole, and the wind has just carried your ball out of bounds.

ANSWER: Well, I didn't hit him when he sneered. I carried the ball within bounds.

"Shooting three," I said calmly. I topped the ball. Gentlemen, I have seen Walter Hagen top the ball the same way.

"Too bad, Professor," said Doc Green. He said it hypocritically. I knew it was hypocrisy. He was secretly gratified that I had topped the ball. He knew I knew it.

QUESTION: What were your emotions at this further insult, Professor?

ANSWER: I pitied him. I thought how inferior he was to me intellectually, and I pitied him. I addressed the ball again. "I pity him," I murmured. "Pity, pity, pity, pity, pity!"

He overheard me. "Your pity has cost you five more strokes," he said.

"I was merely gesticulating," I said.

QUESTION: Did the ball move? Remember, you are under oath, and you have waived immunity.

ANSWER: If the ball moved, it was because a strong breeze had sprung up.

QUESTION: Go on.

ANSWER: I laid the ball upon the green and again holed out with one putt. "I'm taking a five," I said, marking it on my card.

"I'm giving you a ten," he said, marking it on his card. "Five gesticulations on account of your pity."

QUESTION: Describe your reactions to this terrible injustice, Professor. Was there a red mist before your eyes? Did you turn giddy and wake up to find him lying lifeless at your feet? Just what happened?

ANSWER: Nothing, sir.

(*Sensation in the grand jury room.*)

QUESTION: Think again, Professor. Nothing?

ANSWER: I merely reflected that, in spite of his standing scientifically, Dr. James T. Green was a moron and utterly devoid of morality and that I should take this into account. I did not lose my temper.

QUESTION: Did you snatch the card from his hands?

ANSWER: I took it, sir. I did not snatch it.

QUESTION: And then did you cram it down his throat?

ANSWER: I suggested that he eat it, sir, as it contained a falsehood in black and white, and Dr. Green complied with my request.

QUESTION: Did you lay hands upon him, Professor? Remember, now, we are still talking about the third hole.

ANSWER: I think I did steady him a little by holding him about the neck and throat while he masticated and swallowed the card.

QUESTION: And then what?

ANSWER: Well, gentlemen, after that there is very little more to tell until we reached the sixteenth hole. Dr. Green for some time made no further attempt to treat me unjustly and played in silence, acquiescing in the scores I had marked on my card. We were even as to holes, and it was a certainty that I was about to break a hundred. But I knew what was beneath this silence on Doc Green's part, and I did not trust it.

QUESTION: What do you mean? That you knew what he was thinking, although he did not speak?

ANSWER: Yes, sir. I knew just what kind of remarks he would have made if he had made any remarks.

QUESTION: Were these remarks which he suppressed derogatory remarks?

ANSWER: Yes, sir. Almost unbelievably so. They were deliberately intended to destroy my poise.

QUESTION: Did they do so, Professor?

ANSWER: I don't think so.

QUESTION: Go on, Professor.

ANSWER: At the sixteenth tee, as I drove off, this form of insult reached its climax. He accentuated his silence with a peculiar look, just as my club head was about to meet the ball. I knew what he meant. He knew that I knew it, and that I knew. I sliced into a bunker. He stood and watched me, as I stepped into the sand with my niblick—watched me with that look upon his face. I made three strokes at the ball and, as will sometimes happen even to the best of players, did not move it a foot. The fourth stroke drove it out of sight into the sand. The sixth stroke brought it to light again. Gentlemen, I did not lose my temper. I never do. But I admit that I did increase my tempo. I struck rapidly three more times at the ball. And all the time Doc Green was regarding me with that look, to which he now added a smile. Still I kept my temper, and he might be alive today if he had not spoken.

QUESTION (*by the foreman of the jury*): What did the man say at this trying time?

ANSWER: I know that you will not believe it is within the human heart to make the black remark that he made. And I hesitate to repeat it. But I have sworn to tell everything. What he said was, "Well, Professor, the club puts these bunkers here, and I suppose they have got to be used."

QUESTION (*by the foreman of the jury*): Was there something especially trying in the way he said it?

ANSWER: There was. He said it with an affectation of joviality.

QUESTION: You mean as if he thought he were making a joke, Professor?

ANSWER: Yes, sir.

QUESTION: What were your emotions at this point?

ANSWER: Well, sir, it came to me suddenly that I owed a duty to society; and for the sake of civilization I struck him with the niblick. It was an effort to reform him, gentlemen.

QUESTION: Why did you cover him with sand afterwards?

ANSWER: Well, I knew that if the crowd around the locker room discovered that I had hit him, they would insist on counting it as another stroke. And that is exactly what happened when the body was discovered—once again I was prevented from breaking a hundred.

THE DISTRICT ATTORNEY: Gentlemen of the jury, you have heard Professor Waddems' frank and open testimony in the case of Dr. James T. Green. My own recommendation is that he be not only released, but complimented, as far as this count is returned. If ever a homicide was justifiable, this one was. And I suggest that you report no indictment against the Professor, without leaving your seats. Many of you will wish to get in at least nine holes before dinner. Tomorrow Professor Waddems will tell us what he knows about the case of Silas W. Amherst, the banker.

DON MARQUIS wanted to be recognized as a writer of "serious" poetry and plays. He once remarked, "It would be one on me if I should be remembered longest for creating a cockroach character." In his heart he must have known it would be so. Archy the cockroach is one of the most famous figures in American humor. E. B. White, as an excited young writer newly arrived in New York City, used to "hang around the corner of Chambers Street and Broadway, thinking: 'Somewhere in that building is the typewriter that archy the cockroach jumps on at night.' "

Donald Robert Perry Marquis was born in 1878 in Illinois. As a young man he held down various jobs—clerk, schoolteacher, hay-baler, actor. Finally he got a job in Washington, D.C., working for the U.S. Bureau of the Census. That led to a part-time reporting job on a Washington newspaper. Then he met Joel Chandler Harris, author of the Uncle Remus stories, who was at that time editor of the Atlanta *Constitution*. Harris encouraged Don Marquis, and gave him a job writing editorials for the *Constitution* and editing *Uncle Remus' Magazine*.

In 1912 Marquis joined the staff of the New York *Sun*, and began to write a column called "The Sun Dial." Here it was that archy and his office-mate, mehitabel the cat, made their debut. Archy emerged late at night and typed out his thoughts by jumping on the keys of Marquis's typewriter. Marquis published the results in his column.

Don Marquis died in 1937, after many years of illness and disappointment about his writing. Only his archy and mehitabel books are in print today. But a book called *The Best of Don Marquis* can be found in libraries, and it includes a number of other kinds of humorous writing by the man who made a cockroach famous.

ALEX ATKINSON

Chapter the Last

Merriman Explains

It must have been a full twelve and a half seconds before anybody broke the stunned silence that followed Merriman's calm announcement. As I look back, I can still see the half-humorous smile playing about his satyr's face in the flickering firelight. I can hear again the hearty cracks he made as he pulled his fingers one by one. I couldn't help feeling that the old fox was holding something back. What lay behind the quizzical look he fired at Eleanor? Did I detect a flutter of fear on her pasty (but somehow curiously attractive) face? What was the significance of the third onion? *Was there a third onion at all? If so, who had it?* These and eight other questions chased themselves around in my brain as I watched

Merriman pick up his Chartreuse and look round at us with quiet amusement.

It was Humphrey who spoke first, his voice echoing strangely through the quiet room, with its crossed swords, Rembrandts, and jade. "But—great Scott!—if Alastair Tripp *wasn't there . . . !"*

"Alastair Tripp," said Merriman, breathing on his monocle (the only time I ever saw him do such a thing in all the years I knew him), "wasn't, as you say, there. *And yet, in a way, he was."*

Humphrey gave a snort of disgust, and drained his crème-de-menthe noisily. Even Chief Inspector Rodd gave vent to a half-stifled groan of bewilderment.

Merriman frowned. "You really are the dumbest crew I ever struck," he snarled. His gay wit was so infectious that the tension eased at once. He pointed at Humphrey with an olive on the end of an ebony-handled poniard. "Take your mind back," he said, "to a week last Wednesday, at sixteen minutes past seven p.m., in the hall of Mossburn Manor. Haven't you realized yet that the Mrs. Ogilvie who flung the grand-father clock over the banisters was in reality her own step-mother—Eleanor's sister's aunt by marriage? Even by the light of a single candle you should have noticed the blonde wig, the false hands, or the papier-mâché mask—*the very mask which was found later up the chimney in Simon's bedroom!* Don't you see?"

Eleanor gasped. I could see Humphrey's knuckles whiten as his bony hands tightened their grip on the handle of the lawn-mower. I felt that the pieces were beginning to drop into place like bits of an enormous, sinister jig-saw puzzle. The trouble was, they didn't seem to fit.

"A left shoe, my half-wits," rumbled Merriman. "A left shoe with the lace missing. One onion where there should have been three. A half-chewed sweet in an otherwise deserted goldfish-bowl. By thunder, surely you *see?*" He rose to his feet and began to pace the room, with his head bent to avoid the oak beams. Sometimes as he walked he trod on the Chief Inspector, and once as he stood upright to emphasize a point, he brought down the chandelier with a crash. "It was a chance remark from Lady Powder that tipped me off," he bellowed, pounding a huge fist on the top of Eleanor's head. Eleanor's eyes widened, and on her face there was a look I hadn't seen before. "We were on the roof, you remember, trying to find a croquet ball, and all of a sudden she said 'It hasn't rained since Monday.' " He stood in the middle of the room, with one hand on the picture-rail and the other in his trousers pocket, and surveyed us. "From that moment," he said quietly, "I knew I was on the wrong track." He started to walk about again, and some of the floor-boards didn't seem any too safe down at my end of the room.

"But—great Scott!—if Alastair Tripp *wasn't there* . . ." Humphrey began again.

"I'm coming to that." Merriman fixed me with his eccentric glare. "I believe I have told you more than once, my foolish ape," he said, "that there are a hundred and four ways of getting into a room with no doors on the inside and no windows on the outside. But that's beside the point. Consider, if you will, the night of the murder. Here we have John Smith taking a nap in the pantry. The door is locked. The window is locked. The cupboard is bare. The carpet—and mark this—the carpet is *rolled up in a corner,* tied round with ordinary common or garden string. Now then, in the first place, as you will have guessed, the lightly-sleeping figure on the camp bed was not John Smith at all." Merriman fixed Eleanor with a penetrating stare. *"You* know who it was, don't you, *Mrs. Anstruther?"*

"Mrs. *what!"* The question left my lips before I could stop it. Eleanor turned deathly pale, and tore her cambric handkerchief in two with a convulsive movement. Chief Inspector Rodd stirred slightly in his sleep. A frown of impatience played fitfully over the chiselled features of Humphrey Beeton. Outside the rain whispered eerily against the panes.

"Good Kensington Gore!" swore Merriman, wrenching a handful of stops from his treasured organ and hurling them at the Chief Inspector: "it was so *easy!"* He sat suddenly in the wicker armchair, and all but flattened Professor Meak, whom we had somehow forgotten. "Let me take you through it step by step. A bootlace is fastened to one end of the blow-pipe, which has previously been filled with sugar. This whole deadly contraption is lowered down the chimney—oh, there was plenty of time, I assure you: remember that Mercia Foxglove had been concealed in the shrubbery since dawn, and in any case at that time nobody knew that Paul's father was really Janet's uncle from Belfast."

"But if Alastair Tripp *wasn't there* . . ." Humphrey's voice was desperate with curiosity. The lawn-mower trembled in his hands.

"I'm coming to that," said Merriman, filling his pipe with herbs. "Three onions," he went on steadily, "have already been placed midway between the door and the golf-club—which, you will observe, is leaning unnoticed against the wall. Very well, then. Recall, if you will, the evidence of the so-called Alfred Harp—actually, of course, as I will show you, he is none other than our friend the mysterious 'milk-man': but more of that anon. Where did he find the decanter after—I repeat, *after*—the gardener's cottage had been burnt to the ground? He found it, my pretty dumbbells, in the pocket of Sir Herbert's dressing-gown—*which was nowhere to be found."* He beamed expansively. *"Now* do you understand?"

Humphrey rose unsteadily. His face was working, and I thought I detected a fleck of foam on his tie. I reached unobtrusively for my hat. "But if Alastair Tripp—*wasn't there—"* Humphrey almost shouted.

"I'm coming to that."

It was too much. With a mighty roar of rage and impatience, Humphrey swung the lawn-mower over his head in a flashing arc.

As I groped my way down the back stairs I reflected sadly that this would probably go down in history as Merriman's Last Case.

ALEX ATKINSON was one of the delightful successes produced by Liverpool long before the Beatles made that city famous as the world's center of irreverent jokes. He was born there in 1916, and started out his adult life as a shoe salesman. After World War II service as a soldier, he acted with the Harrogate Repertory Company—learning a number of parts in different plays and performing them on tours to outlying cities and towns.

In 1948 Atkinson began contributing to *Punch,* a magazine of wit and humor that weekly sends the English into fits of discreet laughter. Four books, illustrated by the English artist Ronald Searle, were compiled from Atkinson's contributions to *Punch.* He also became known as a novelist and playwright.

In 1960 Atkinson came to the United States to join the staff of *Holiday* magazine as associate editor. He died two years later, in Philadelphia.

Any reader of mystery novels or viewer of detective movies will recognize in "Chapter the Last" the conventional final scene in which "whodunit" is disclosed. Atkinson was adept at parody, a sneaky form of writing that makes fun of a subject by imitation —but imitation with a twist. Readers with a taste for parody will find an unsurpassed collection of them in *Parodies,* compiled by Dwight Macdonald.

E. B. WHITE

The Color of Mice

Nothing pleases me more than an old belt. When age has limbered it, a belt grows increasingly precious, for in its abandoned notches a man traces the lively story of his youth. I need only look at the first knife-punched hole in my belt to read a whole saga of the girded loin and remember how, in the presence of other boys, I used to hitch myself tight with a jerk of bravado and a slight pain in the stomach. An old belt like that is not to be lightly discarded, merely because it's old.

Probably my wife did not realize how I felt about belts when she called me across the room the other evening.

"What is that leather thing holding your pants up?" she asked.

"That's my old belt and we won't go into it any further," I replied. "It is *my* belt, it is comfortable, and it reminds me of days gone by."

"Well," she said, "it reminds me of old pieces of rope, old window-shade tassels, and old halters that are found after barns burn down. Take it off and buy yourself a new one."

"Not the slightest chance," I remarked.

"Well, then, wear a vest. You can't go around looking like that."

We did not discuss belts any more that evening. We might, in truth, never have discussed belts again all our lives had not I gone into a haberdasher's shop the next morning to buy a shirt because my clean ones had run out. I noticed that the salesman, whom I did not like, eyed me as he wrapped the parcel—much as my wife had eyed me the night before. As I started to go, he came round the corner of the counter, stealthily. He took my arm.

"Can I interest you in a belt?" he asked.

What transpired from then on is just what transpires in hundreds of haberdasheries every day in the week—the native resolution, the faltering voice, the lure of the article, the glittering eye, the gradual breaking down of the spirit, the ultimate sale, the whimpering, broken man going out through the door with an extra parcel under his arm. Only in my case it was worse, because the clerk not only sold me a belt, he sold me a mouse-gray belt. He said mouse-gray was the thing.

All day at the office I wore my old belt. But on the way upstairs to the apartment I slipped the new one on, fretfully aware that the notch was not in the right place, annoyed at the strange pressure and the stiffness.

"Now what have you done?" said my wife, when I took my coat off.

"Well, who started all this belt trouble, anyway?" I wanted to know. "You said get a new belt, so I did."

"No, you didn't," she replied, "because that thing is going right back where it came from, so take it off quick before the notch gets noticeable."

"Listen," I began, "this belt is mouse-gray, and if you knew anything at all you'd know that mouse-gray is the thing."

"Come over here, my little man," said my wife. So I went over. "Now don't you realize that you'll get into trouble with that belt?"

"What d'you mean, trouble?"

"I mean it may attract mice."

"You make me sick," I said. "Anyway, it isn't exactly a mouse-gray—it's more a battleship-gray."

"Well, it may attract battleships," said my wife, who thinks she is funny. Again we dropped the discussion, and I went to sleep that night vowing to wear the new gray belt for a few days merely as a gesture, and then work gradually back into my old one later. But this is really where my story begins.

I had hardly got to the bottom of the stairs next morning, when I looked down and saw that a little mouse was following me.

"G'wan!" I cried, waving my *Herald Tribune* at him. "Git out of here!" But he still came on, scurrying along from step to step, nose to the ground. "Hey!" I screamed, rushing through the door and down the street toward the Elevated. As I passed the Greek's on the corner, another mouse ran out and joined the first. The two of them came bristling up the Elevated steps, right at my heels, and on the platform one of them boldly started up my trouser-leg. "Phoo! You can't do that!" I yelled, swatting the climbing one. But the words had barely rung out across the morning when a third mouse leapt from the old stove in the ticket office and began to advance toward me.

I rode uptown with the three of them under my coat, snuggled against my belt, and pretended bravely that I was enjoying the editorials in the paper.

At Forty-second Street I got off, quite frightened, and wondering what my next move would be. I wished I had paid some attention to my wife, but there was very little time to think about her. People were already beginning to notice that I had mice. Some of the women in the "L" station were screaming, in a fragmentary way. Dodge along as I might, I could not elude the three little mice, and they came leaping and playing down the steps with me to the street.

For a moment I just stood still on the sidewalk. I did not dare take my belt off for fear my trousers would come down; it seemed to me that would be worse than mice. It did not particularly surprise me that a fourth mouse appeared from under the news-stand and climbed my leg—worse than the others in his fresh frenzy to get at my mouse-colored belt.

Even in my bewilderment I could not help noticing that the town, at Forty-second Street and Sixth Avenue, seemed to be noisier than usual. The roar of the "L," the banging of the crosstown cars, the grinding of horns, the screams of the terrified women leaping out of the way of my mice—these sounds were dimmed in a mighty crashing sound that seemed to be coming from the general direction of Riverside Drive.

It grew louder as I stood there, and it soon became mingled with the distant sound of shattered glass and falling timbers and twisting steel. I looked upward. The sky was full of black smoke. I had a feeling that I was being swept back into another period, a glacial time. I had a feeling that I didn't even know what the little boy was talking about who came racing madly down Sixth Avenue, screaming "Battleships!"

It was all true. The battleships were coming—mowing down everything before them in their relentless haste to get to my belt. Already I could see the sun glint from their wet sides, the lean guns advancing, the knife-blades of the prows, the belching stacks clouding the sky. With only one course left open, I lost no time.

"Take this," I said, slipping off my belt and handing it to the nearest lady, before she could see that there were some mice that went with it. As I did so, my trousers rippled to the ground and I sprang, half naked and wholly nimble, into the nearest haberdashery. With no surprise at all I heard an unctuous voice begin, "Can I interest you in some B.V.D.'s?"

A biographical sketch of E. B. White will be found following the selection "What Should Children Tell Parents?"

STEPHEN LEACOCK

My Financial Career

When I go into a bank I get rattled. The clerks rattle me; the wickets rattle me; the sight of the money rattles me; everything rattles me.

The moment I cross the threshold of a bank and attempt to transact business there, I become an irresponsible idiot.

I knew this beforehand, but my salary had been raised to fifty dollars a month and I felt that the bank was the only place for it.

So I shambled in and looked timidly round at the clerks. I had an idea that a person about to open an account must needs consult the manager.

I went up to a wicket marked "Accountant." The accountant was a tall, cool devil. The very sight of him rattled me. My voice was sepulchral.

"Can I see the manager?" I said, and added solemnly, "alone." I don't know why I said "alone."

"Certainly," said the accountant, and fetched him.

The manager was a grave, calm man. I held my fifty-six dollars clutched in a crumpled ball in my pocket.

"Are you the manager?" I said. God knows I didn't doubt it.

"Yes," he said.

"Can I see you," I asked, "alone?" I didn't want to say "alone" again, but without it the thing seemed self-evident.

The manager looked at me in some alarm. He felt that I had an awful secret to reveal.

"Come in here," he said, and led the way to a private room. He turned the key in the lock.

"We are safe from interruption here," he said; "sit down."

We both sat down and looked at each other. I found no voice to speak.

"You are one of Pinkerton's men, I presume," he said.

He had gathered from my mysterious manner that I was a detective. I knew what he was thinking, and it made me worse.

"No, not from Pinkerton's," I said, seeming to imply that I came from a rival agency.

"To tell the truth," I went on, as if I had been prompted to lie about it, "I am not a detective at all. I have come to open an account. I intend to keep all my money in this bank."

The manager looked relieved but still serious; he concluded now that I was a son of Baron Rothschild or a young Gould.

"A large account, I suppose," he said.

"Fairly large," I whispered. "I propose to deposit fifty-six dollars now and fifty dollars a month regularly."

The manager got up and opened the door. He called to the accountant.

"Mr. Montgomery," he said unkindly loud, "this gentleman is opening an account, he will deposit fifty-six dollars. Good morning."

I rose.

A big iron door stood open at the side of the room.

"Good morning," I said, and stepped into the safe.

"Come out," said the manager coldly, and showed me the other way.

I went up to the accountant's wicket and poked the ball of money at him with a quick convulsive movement as if I were doing a conjuring trick.

My face was ghastly pale.

"Here," I said, "deposit it." The tone of the words seemed to mean, "Let us do this painful thing while the fit is on us."

He took the money and gave it to another clerk.

He made me write the sum on a slip and sign my name in a book. I no longer knew what I was doing. The bank swam before my eyes.

"Is it deposited?" I asked in a hollow, vibrating voice.

"It is," said the accountant.

"Then I want to draw a check."

My idea was to draw out six dollars of it for present use. Someone gave me a check-book through a wicket and someone else began telling me how to write it out. The people in the bank had the impression that I was an invalid millionaire. I wrote something on the check and thrust it in at the clerk. He looked at it.

"What! are you drawing it all out again?" he asked in surprise.

Then I realized that I had written fifty-six instead of six. I was too far gone to reason now. I had a feeling that it was impossible to explain the thing. All the clerks had stopped writing to look at me.

Reckless with misery, I made a plunge.

"Yes, the whole thing."

"You withdraw your money from the bank?"

"Every cent of it."

"Are you not going to deposit any more?" said the clerk, astonished.

"Never."

An idiot hope struck me that they might think something had insulted me while I was writing the check and that I had changed my mind. I made a wretched attempt to look like a man with a fearfully quick temper.

The clerk prepared to pay the money.

"How will you have it?" he said.

"What?"

"How will you have it?"

"Oh"—I caught his meaning and answered without even trying to think—"in fifties."

He gave me a fifty-dollar bill.

"And the six?" he asked dryly.

"In sixes," I said.

He gave it me and I rushed out.

As the big door swung behind me I caught the echo of a roar of laughter that went up to the ceiling of the bank. Since then I bank no more. I keep my money in cash in my trousers pocket and my savings in silver dollars in a sock.

STEPHEN LEACOCK was a respected professor of political science until he began writing humorous stories. Friends encouraged him to publish the stories. One day he gathered the sketches together and sent them to the publishers of his book *Political Economy*. As he told it, "They thought I had gone mad." He never seemed to mind being thought mad, however. He said, "I would rather have written *Alice in Wonderland* than the whole *Encyclopaedia Britannica*."

Leacock was born in England in 1869. His family moved to Canada when he was seven, and he grew up and went to school there. From 1903 until his retirement in 1936, he taught political science at McGill University in Canada. He died in 1944.

In addition to his many scholarly works on political science, economics, and history, Leacock also wrote biographies of two of his favorite humorists, Mark Twain and Charles Dickens. His funny writing is available in *Laugh with Leacock, Leacock Roundabout,* and several other books.

RING LARDNER

I Can't Breathe

July 12

I am staying here at the Inn for two weeks with my Uncle
Nat and Aunt Jule and I think I will keep a kind of a diary
while I am here to help pass the time and so I can have a
record of things that happen though goodness knows there
isn't lightly to anything happen, that is anything exciting
with Uncle Nat and Aunt Jule making the plans as they are
both at least 35 years old and maybe older.

Dad and mother are abroad to be gone a month and me
coming here is supposed to be a recompence for them not
taking me with them. A fine recompence to be left with old
people that come to a place like this to rest. Still it would be a
heavenly place under different conditions, for instance if

Walter were here, too. It would be heavenly if he were here, the very thought of it makes my heart stop.

I can't stand it. I won't think about it.

This is our first seperation since we have been engaged, nearly 17 days. It will 17 days tomorrow. And the hotel orchestra at dinner this evening played that old thing "Oh how I miss you tonight" and it seemed as if they must be playing it for my benefit though of course the person in that song is talking about how they miss their mother though of course I miss mother too, but a person gets used to missing their mother and it isn't like Walter or the person you are engaged to.

But there won't be any more seperations much longer, we are going to be married in December even if mother does laugh when I talk to her about it because she says I am crazy to even think of getting married at 18.

She got married herself when she was 18, but of course that was "different," she wasn't crazy like I am, she knew whom she was marrying. As if Walter were a policeman or a foreigner or something. And she says she was only engaged once while I have been engaged at least five times a year since I was 14, of course it really isn't as bad as that and I have really only been really what I call engaged six times altogether, but is getting engaged my fault when they keep insisting and hammering at you and if you didn't say yes they would never go home.

But it is different with Walter. I honestly believe if he had not asked me I would have asked him. Of course I wouldn't have, but I would have died. And this is the first time I have ever been engaged to be really married. The other times when they talked about when should we get married I just laughed at them, but I hadn't been engaged to Walter ten minutes when he brought up the subject of marriage and I didn't laugh. I wouldn't be engaged to him unless it was to be married. I couldn't stand it.

Anyway mother may as well get used to the idea because it is "No Foolin'" this time and we have got our plans all made and I am going to be married at home and go out to California and Hollywood on our honeymoon. December, five months away. I can't stand it. I can't wait.

There were a couple of awfully nice looking boys sitting together alone in the dining-room tonight. One of them wasn't so much, but the other was cute. And he——

There's the dance orchestra playing "Always," what they played at the Biltmore the day I met Walter. "Not for just an hour not for just a day." I can't live. I can't breathe.

July 13

This has been a much more exciting day than I expected under the circumstances. In the first place I got two long night letters, one from Walter and one from Gordon Flint. I don't see how Walter ever had the nerve to send his, there was everything in it and it must have been horribly embarrassing for him while the telegraph operator was reading it over and counting the words to say nothing of embarrassing for the operator.

But the one from Gordon was a kind of a shock. He just got back from a trip around the world, left last December to go on it and got back yesterday and called up our house and Helga gave him my address, and his telegram, well it was nearly as bad as Walter's. The trouble is that Gordon and I were engaged when he went away, or at least he thought so and he wrote to me right along all the time he was away and sent cables and things and for a while I answered his letters, but then I lost track of his itinery and couldn't write to him any more and when I got really engaged to Walter I couldn't let Gordon know because I had no idea where he was besides not wanting to spoil his trip.

And now he still thinks we are engaged and he is going to call me up tomorrow from Chicago and how in the world can I explain things and get him to understand because he is really serious and I like him ever and ever so much and in lots of ways he is nicer than Walter, not really nicer but better looking and there is no comparison between their dancing. Walter simply can't learn to dance, that is really dance. He says it is because he is flat footed, he says that as a joke, but it is true and I wish to heavens it wasn't.

All forenoon I thought and thought and thought about what to say to Gordon when he calls up and finally I couldn't stand thinking about it any more and just made up my mind I wouldn't think about it any more. But I will tell the truth though it will kill me to hurt him.

I went down to lunch with Uncle Nat and Aunt Jule and they were going out to play golf this afternoon and were insisting that I go with them, but I told them I had a headache and then I had a terrible time getting them to go without me. I didn't have a headache at all and just wanted to be alone to think about Walter and besides when you play with Uncle Nat he is always correcting your stance or your swing or something and always puts his hands on my arms or shoulders to show me the right way and I can't stand it to have old men touch me, even if they are your uncle.

I finally got rid of them and I was sitting watching the

tennis when that boy that I saw last night, the cute one, came and sat right next to me and of course I didn't look at him and I was going to smoke a cigarette and found I had left my lighter upstairs and I started to get up and go after it when all of a sudden he was offering me his lighter and I couldn't very well refuse it without being rude. So we got to talking and he is even cuter than he looks, the most original and wittiest person I believe I ever met and I haven't laughed so much in I don't know how long.

For one thing he asked me if I had heard Rockefeller's song and I said no and he began singing "Oil alone." Then he asked me if I knew the orange juice song and I told him no again and he said it was "Orange juice sorry you made me cry." I was in hysterics before we had been together ten minutes.

His name is Frank Caswell and he has been out of Dartmouth a year and is 24 years old. That isn't so terribly old, only two years older than Walter and three years older than Gordon. I hate the name Frank, but Caswell is all right and he is so cute.

He was out in California last winter and visited Hollywood and met everybody in the world and it is fascinating to listen to him. He met Norma Shearer and he said he thought she was the prettiest thing he had ever seen. What he said was "I did think she was the priettiest girl in the world, till today." I was going to pretend I didn't get it, but I finally told him to be sensible or I would never be able to believe anything he said.

Well, he wanted me to dance with him tonight after dinner and the next question was how to explain how we had met each other to Uncle Nat and Aunt Jule. Frank said he would fix that all right and sure enough he got himself introduced to Uncle Nat when Uncle Nat came in from golf and after dinner Uncle Nat introduced him to me and Aunt Jule too and we danced together all evening, that is not Aunt Jule. They went to bed, thank heavens.

He is a heavenly dancer, as good as Gordon. One dance we were dancing and for one of the encores the orchestra played "In a cottage small by a waterfall" and I simply couldn't dance to it. I just stopped still and said "Listen, I can't bear it, I can't breathe" and poor Frank thought I was sick or something and I had to explain that that was the tune the orchestra played the night I sat at the next table to Jack Barrymore at Barney Gallant's.

I made him sit out that encore and wouldn't let him talk till they got through playing it. Then they played something else and I was all right again and Frank told me about meeting Jack Barrymore. Imagine meeting him. I couldn't live.

I promised Aunt Jule I would go to bed at eleven and it is way past that now, but I am all ready for bed and have just been writing this. Tomorrow Gordon is going to call up and what will I say to him? I just won't think about it.

July 14

Gordon called up this morning from Chicago and it was wonderful to hear his voice again though the connection was terrible. He asked me if I still loved him and I tried to tell him no, but I knew that would mean an explanation and the connection was so bad that I never could make him understand so I said yes, but I almost whispered it purposely, thinking he wouldn't hear me, but he heard me all right and he said that made everything all right with the world. He said he thought I had stopped loving him because I had stopped writing.

I wish the connection had been decent and I could have told him how things were, but now it is terrible because he is planning to get to New York the day I get there and heaven knows what I will do because Walter will be there, too. I just won't think about it.

Aunt Jule came in my room just after I was through talking to Gordon, thank heavens. The room was full of flowers. Walter had sent me some and so had Frank. I got another long night letter from Walter, just as silly as the first one. I wish he would say those things in letters instead of night letters so everybody in the world wouldn't see them. Aunt Jule wanted me to read it aloud to her. I would have died.

While she was still in the room, Frank called up and asked me to play golf with him and I said all right and Aunt Jule said she was glad my headache was gone. She was trying to be funny.

I played golf with Frank this afternoon. He is a beautiful golfer and it is thrilling to watch him drive, his swing is so much more graceful than Walter's. I asked him to watch me swing and tell me what was the matter with me, but he said he couldn't look at anything but my face and there wasn't anything the matter with that.

He told me the boy who was here with him had been called home and he was glad of it because I might have liked him, the other boy, better than himself. I told him that couldn't be possible and he asked me if I really meant that and I said of course, but I smiled when I said it so he wouldn't take it too seriously.

We danced again tonight and Uncle Nat and Aunt Jule sat with us a while and danced a couple of dances themselves, but they were really there to get better acquainted with Frank and see if he was all right for me to be with. I know they certainly couldn't have enjoyed their own dancing, no old people really can enjoy it because they can't really *do* anything.

They were favorably impressed with Frank I think, at least Aunt Jule didn't say I must be in bed at eleven, but just not to stay up too late. I guess it is a big surprise to a girl's parents and aunts and uncles to find out that the boys you go around with are all right, they always seem to think that if I seem to like somebody and the person pays a little attention to me, why he must be a convict or a policeman or a drunkard or something queer.

Frank had some more songs for me tonight. He asked me if I knew the asthma song and I said I didn't and he said "Oh, you must know that. It goes yes, sir, asthma baby." Then he told me about the underwear song, "I underwear my baby is tonight." He keeps you in hysterics and yet he has his serious side, in fact he was awfully serious when he said good night to me and his eyes simply shown. I wish Walter were more like him in some ways, but I mustn't think about that.

July 15

I simply can't live and I know I'll never sleep tonight. I am in a terrible predicament or rather I won't know whether I really am or not till tomorrow and that is what makes it so terrible.

After we had danced two or three dances, Frank asked me to go for a ride with him and we went for a ride in his car and he had had some cocktails and during the ride he had some drinks out of a flask and finally he told me he loved me and I said not to be silly, but he said he was perfectly serious and he certainly acted that way. He asked me if I loved anybody else and I said yes and he asked if I didn't love him more than anybody else and I said yes, but only because I thought he had probably had too much to drink and wouldn't remember it anyway and the best thing to do was humor him under the circumstances.

Then all of a sudden he asked me when I could marry him and I said, just as a joke, that I couldn't possibly marry him before December. He said that was a long time to wait, but I was certainly worth waiting for and he said a lot of other things and maybe I humored him a little too much, but that is just the trouble, I don't know.

I was absolutely sure he was tight and would forget the whole thing, but that was early in the evening, and when we said good night he was a whole lot more sober than he had been and now I am not sure how it stands. If he doesn't remember anything about it, of course I am all right. But if he does remember and if he took me seriously, I will simply have to tell him about Walter and maybe about Gordon, too. And it isn't going to be easy. The suspense is what is maddening and I know I'll never live through this night.

July 16

I can't stand it, I can't breathe, life is impossible. Frank remembered everything about last night and firmly believes we are engaged and going to be married in December. His people live in New York and he says he is going back when I do and have them meet me.

Of course it can't go on and tomorrow I will tell him about Walter or Gordon or both of them. I know it is going to hurt him terribly, perhaps spoil his life and I would give anything in the world not to have had it happen. I hate so to hurt him because he is so nice besides being so cute and attractive.

He sent me the loveliest flowers this morning and called up at ten and wanted to know how soon he could see me and I hope the girl wasn't listening in because the things he said were, well like Walter's night letters.

And that is another terrible thing, today I didn't get a night letter from Walter, but there was a regular letter instead and I carried it around in my purse all this afternoon and evening and never remembered to read it till ten minutes ago when I came up in the room. Walter is worried because I have only sent him two telegrams and written him one letter since I have been here, he would be a lot more worried if he knew what has happened now, though of course it can't make any difference because he is the one I am really engaged to be married to and the one I told mother I was going to marry in December and I wouldn't dare tell her it was somebody else.

I met Frank for lunch and we went for a ride this afternoon and he was so much in love and so lovely to me that I simply did not have the heart to tell him the truth, I am surely going to tell him tomorrow and telling him today would have just meant one more day of unhappiness for both of us.

He said his people had plenty of money and his father

had offered to take him into partnership and he might accept, but he thinks his true vocation is journalism with a view to eventually writing novels and if I was willing to undergo a few hardships just at first we would probably both be happier later on if he was doing something he really liked. I didn't know what to say, but finally I said I wanted him to suit himself and money wasn't everything.

He asked me where I would like to go on my honeymoon and I suppose I ought to have told him my honeymoon was all planned, that I was going to California, with Walter, but all I said was that I had always wanted to go to California and he was enthusiastic and said that is where we would surely go and he would take me to Hollywood and introduce me to all those wonderful people he met there last winter. It nearly takes my breath away to think of it, going there with someone who really knows people and has the entrée.

We danced again tonight, just two or three dances, and then went out and sat in the tennis-court, but I came upstairs early because Aunt Jule had acted kind of funny at dinner. And I wanted to be alone, too, and think, but the more I think the worse it gets.

Sometimes I wish I were dead, maybe that is the only solution and it would be best for everyone concerned. I *will* die if things keep on the way they have been. But of course tomorrow it will be all over, with Frank I mean, for I must tell him the truth no matter how much it hurts us both. Though I don't care how much it hurts me. The thought of hurting him is what is driving me mad. I can't bear it.

July 18

I have skipped a day. I was busy every minute of yesterday and so exhausted when I came upstairs that I was tempted to fall into bed with all my clothes on. First Gordon called me up from Chicago to remind me that he would be in New York the day I got there and that when he comes he wants me all to himself all the time and we can make plans for our wedding. The connection was bad again and I just couldn't explain to him about Walter.

I had an engagement with Frank for lunch and just as we were going in another long distance call came, from Walter this time. He wanted to know why I haven't written more letters and sent him more telegrams and asked me if I still loved him and of course I told him yes because I really do. Then he asked if I had met any men here and I told him I had met one, a friend of Uncle Nat's. After all it was Uncle Nat who introduced me to Frank. He reminded me that he would be in New York on the 25th which is the day I expect to get home, and said he would have theater tickets for that night and we would go somewhere afterwards and dance.

Frank insisted on knowing who had kept me talking so long and I told him it was a boy I had known a long while, a very dear friend of mine and a friend of my family's. Frank was jealous and kept asking questions till I thought I would go mad. He was so serious and kind of cross and gruff that I gave up the plan of telling him the truth till some time when he is in better spirits.

I played golf with Frank in the afternoon and we took a ride last night and I wanted to get in early because I had promised both Walter and Gordon that I would write them

long letters, but Frank wouldn't bring me back to the Inn till
I had named a definite date in December. I finally told him
the 10th and he said all right if I was sure that wasn't a
Sunday. I said I would have to look it up, but as a matter of
fact I know the 10th falls on a Friday because the date Walter
and I have agreed on for our wedding is Saturday the 11th.

Today has just been the same thing over again, two
more night letters, a long distance call from Chicago, golf and
a ride with Frank, and the room full of flowers. But tomorrow I am going to tell Frank and I am going to write
Gordon a long letter and tell him, too, because this simply
can't go on any longer. I can't breathe. I can't live.

July 21

I wrote to Gordon yesterday, but I didn't say anything
about Walter because I don't think it is a thing a person
ought to do by letter. I can tell him when he gets to New
York and then I will be sure that he doesn't take it too hard
and I can promise him that I will be friends with him always
and make him promise not to do anything silly, while if I
told it to him in a letter there is no telling what he would do,
there all alone.

And I haven't told Frank because he hasn't been feeling
well, he is terribly sunburned and it hurts him terribly so he
can hardly play golf or dance, and I want him to be feeling
his best when I do tell him, but whether he is all right or not
I simply must tell him tomorrow because he is actually
planning to leave here on the same train with us Saturday
night and I can't let him do that.

Life is so hopeless and it could be so wonderful. For
instance how heavenly it would be if I could marry Frank

first and stay married to him five years and he would be the one who would take me to Hollywood and maybe we could go on parties with Norman Kerry and Jack Barrymore and Buster Collier and Marion Davies and Lois Moran.

And at the end of five years Frank could go into journalism and write novels and I would only be 23 and I could marry Gordon and he would be ready for another trip around the world and he could show me things better than someone who had never seen them before.

Gordon and I would separate at the end of five years and I would be 28 and I know of lots of women that never even got married the first time till they were 28 though I don't suppose that was their fault, but I would marry Walter then, for after all he is the one I really love and want to spend most of my life with and I wouldn't care whether he could dance or not when I was that old. Before long we would be as old as Uncle Nat and Aunt Jule and I certainly wouldn't want to dance at their age when all you can do is just hobble around the floor. But Walter is so wonderful as a companion and we would enjoy the same things and be pals and maybe we would begin to have children.

But that is all impossible though it wouldn't be if older people just had sense and would look at things the right way.

It is only half past ten, the earliest I have gone to bed in weeks, but I am worn out and Frank went to bed early so he could put cold cream on his sunburn.

Listen, diary, the orchestra is playing "Limehouse Blues." The first tune I danced to with Merle Oliver, two years ago. I can't stand it. And how funny that they should play that old tune tonight of all nights, when I have been

thinking of Merle off and on all day, and I hadn't thought of
him before in weeks and weeks. I wonder where he is, I
wonder if it is just an accident or if it means I am going to see
him again. I simply mustn't think about it or I'll die.

July 22

I knew it wasn't an accident. I knew it must mean
something, and it did.

Merle is coming here today, here to this Inn, and just to
see me. And there can only be one reason. And only one
answer. I knew that when I heard his voice calling from
Boston. How could I ever had thought I loved anyone else?
How could he ever have thought I meant it when I told him
I was engaged to George Morse?

A whole year and he still cares and I still care. That
shows we were always intended for each other and for no one
else: I won't make *him* wait till December. I doubt if we
even wait till dad and mother get home. And as for a honeymoon I will go with him to Long Beach or the Bronx Zoo,
wherever he wants to take me.

After all this is the best way out of it, the only way. I
won't have to say anything to Frank, he will guess when he
sees me with Merle. And when I get home Sunday and
Walter and Gordon call me up, I will invite them both to
dinner and Merle can tell them himself, with two of them
there it will only hurt each one half as much as if they were
alone.

The train is due at 2:40, almost three hours from now. I
can't wait. And what if it should be late? I can't stand it.

RING LARDNER was thwarted in his early ambition to go to the University of Michigan "and take football and dentistry." Instead, he flunked out of engineering school. Next, he was fired from his job as a freight agent because he sent a shipment of cream cheese in the wrong direction. These events had no influence on his later life.

Lardner was born in Niles, Michigan, in 1885, and was given the name Ringgold Wilmer Lardner. He did his first writing as a newspaper reporter and as the editor of *Sporting News,* a weekly publication about baseball. One year the Chicago *Examiner* sent Lardner south to cover the Chicago White Sox in spring training. Lardner began to write down the stories told to him by one of the Sox pitchers, Jack Keefe. In 1914 he sent the stories, in the form of funny letters written by a baseball player, to the *Saturday Evening Post.* They were published in the *Post* and later as a book called *You Know Me, Al,* which made Lardner one of the most famous humorists of his time. During the 1920's Lardner published two books of short humorous stories, *How to Write Short Stories* and *The Love Nest.* He also wrote for newspapers and magazines, and collaborated on Broadway shows. He was able to be funny in many forms. The selection here is a "diary," but he also wrote parodies of fairy tales, mock explanations of various sports, zany essays, and several wild nonsense plays, including *Quadroon.*

One writer said that Lardner's gift was an "ability, even a talent, for hating." If that was true, he managed to turn his hate into acid laughter. He was not an unpleasant man. He loved to put people on, and once told an editor that he composed his stories by writing a few widely separated words on a page and then going back and filling in the blanks. He brightened the lives of his friends with funny letters and telegrams, like this one to F. Scott Fitzgerald, who was vacationing in Europe: WHEN ARE YOU COMING BACK AND WHY PLEASE ANSWER.

After several years of poor health, Ring Lardner died at the age of forty-eight. The most ample collection of his work is *The Ring Lardner Reader.*

A. J. LIEBLING

"What Do You Expect for Two Dollars?"

There never were many people in the finest restaurant I ever discovered within the city limits (it was at one of New York's bathing beaches), and most of those there were deemed unwanted. Sometimes a party of four sunburned adults and maybe three children would sit around a table uneasily for half an hour, the men in shirt-sleeves, the women in cotton dresses, and no waiter would come near them. Three or four waiters, old, acrid fellows, would be standing in the farthest corner of the vast room, talking and laughing bitterly, and looking over at the people at the table. The waiters wore black alpaca coats and round tin badges with numbers in them. Once we saw a man at a table grow angry and bang on the water carafe with a knife. There was only yellow, tepid water in the carafe. A waiter shuffled to his table from the far corner. He seemed to take an interminable time getting there, and the *slup-slup* of his broken old shoes on the floor sounded loud in that almost silent place. The man said something to him, and then the waiter said in a loud, contemptuous voice, "We don't serve sandwiches or soft drinks here." The party went out, the men looking ashamed, the women scolding their males for subjecting them to such embarrassment.

"Some of them turf-cutters," our waiter said, flicking crumbs off our table with the end of his napkin. " 'Turf-cutter' is a word we use for cheap Irish," he said, knocking most of the crumbs into my girl's lap. He looked Irish himself. "The Beach is full of them," he said. "Let them go down to the Limerick House."

The restaurant must have been built shortly after the Columbia Exposition. It was an imitation of a cake-frosting exposition building, with seven senseless minarets on it. Most of the white paint had flaked off, or turned grey with age and sea air. The signs about specialties of the house were painted right on the building, in what had once been silver lettering, on what had once been a maroon ground. Evidently the lettering had not been changed since the restaurant was built. Most of the signs said RHODE ISLAND CLAMBAKE, $1.75 or ROAST CHICKEN DINNER, $1.50. In the state to which the Beach has declined, these are high prices. They must have been high forty years ago, too, but then the Beach was a fashionable resort, with a clientele of hot sports. It cost a dollar just to get there from Manhattan, in a steamboat. Now the most dashing attractions are a couple of tired carrousels and a few saloons that advertise in the Irish-American newspapers, but most of the people who come to the Beach do not patronize even them. They just change into their bathing suits under the boardwalk and go swimming, and when they come out, they eat at hot-dog stands. The swimming is good.

The floor of the restaurant sloped like a ship's deck in a big sea. Like all the older buildings at the Beach, it had been built without a foundation, and it had settled in the sand unevenly. The dish covers, the soup tureens, and the rest of the tableware had an antiquarian interest. Each piece bore the name of an old, vanished restaurant: Shanley's, Churchill's, or Jack's.

The restaurant was so obviously decadent and unprosperous that we had not ventured into it the first few times that we went to the Beach to swim. It was only after investigating the possibilities of the Greek lunchrooms, the Japanese waffle shops, and the saloons that we had dared that ghostly pavilion, deciding that we had nothing to lose. The food in the old restaurant had astonished us. The steamed clams were small, clean, and accompanied by a stiff sauce of butter with tarragon vinegar and curry powder blended into it. The chicken fricassee was not smothered in a white flour paste, but yellow and succulent. The $3.50 steak, for two, was perfect. As long as we ordered substantially, took cocktails before dinner, and drank plenty of beer with the meal, the waiters tolerated us.

One evening I ordered a "combination" of steamed clams and a broiled lobster, with potatoes. It had seemed to me that included in this offering, on the menu, was a green salad. Having finished the lobster, I asked for this salad.

The waiter said, "What do you expect for two dollars? A *gold* watch?"

It was this same waiter, however, who on another evening began to talk to me, almost without condescension. It is true he had been drinking.

"The place is a hundred years behind the times," he said. "It's a summer home for broken-down waiters."

He put one hand on our table and leaned his weight on it.

"The cook is forty-nine million years old," he said. "Some day he'll fall into the clam chowder. At the end of every season the old man says to him, 'I never want to see you no more. You're as dead as a doornail.' And at the beginning of the next season he sends a taxicab for him. He used to cook at Burns's. The old man is in his second childhood. That's him setting up on the high stool by the bar. He ain't got no cash register, only an old wooden cashbox. He sets there from ten o'clock in the morning until closing time, to see that no waiter gets away with a glass of beer."

The waiter pointed his chin angrily towards the figure on the stool, diagonally across the room from us. The old gentleman was dressed in a black broadcloth suit, such as a conservative undertaker might wear in winter. The upper part of the vest looked very big for him, but his lower abdomen ballooned out like a spider's. On top of his head he balanced an old Panama hat, coloured like a meerschaum pipe. Even from there we could see how badly he needed a shave.

"He's had that Panama hat for twenty years," the waiter grumbled. "Every spring he has it cleaned, and I think painted, and he brags to everybody he knows about it. 'See,' he says, 'the Panama hat is good for another season.' He's in his second childhood. But try to take a dime off him," the waiter said, "and he ain't in his second childhood no more. You can't do it."

The old man came down off the stool, reluctantly, like a boy sliding into a too-cold swimming pool. He shuffled toward our end of the room, glaring suspiciously over the tops of his spectacles. He had a long, pointed nose. Fifteen feet from our table the old man stopped and stared at us for a minute. Then he turned and went away. Laboriously he climbed up on the stool.

"He was just coming over to see there wasn't too many customers in the place," the waiter explained. "The other night they was lined up two deep at the bar, for once, so he says to the bartender, 'Come out from behind that bar, Joe, and take a walk around the block until they clear out of here.' He don't like no customers. It's second childhood. Do you know what worries him the most? The fear that somebody would park at the curb here. He hates automobiles. So he puts a stepladder in front of the curb and a pot of green paint on top of it. So anybody that drives in will knock the ladder over and get paint on his car. 'Oh, he-he-he,' the old man laughs the last time that happens. 'Look at the damn fool! Too bad he didn't get it on his clothes,' the old man says."

The dining room opens on to a terrace on a level with the sidewalk. We looked out and saw the ladder, with the paintpot perched on the top step.

Another waiter, even older than ours who was pretty old himself, edged up to our man. "I don't like to say nothing,

Murph," he said, "but them people over at that table over there says they give you their order half an hour ago."

"Tell them it's a two-mile walk to the kitchen and back," said our waiter. The people, two men and two women, had been watching him right along, and knew he had not been to the kitchen. When they saw he was not going to do anything about it, they got up and left.

"Deaf as a post the old man is," the waiter went on. "You should hear him talk on the telephone with his sister that lives at the Plaza. 'I'm fine,' he yells as soon as he picks up the phone. He thinks she's asking him how he is. No matter what the hell she calls up to talk to him about, he just says, 'I'm fine,' and hangs up. But if you drop a dollar bill on the floor, he hears it hit."

Perhaps the old man sensed that we were talking about him. Hesitantly, he got down off his stool again and walked over toward us, then stopped, irresolute, at the same point as before, and turned and went back.

"It's on account of him that the Beach is going to hell," said our waiter. "He owns all the property for a mile around, and he won't put a coat of paint on a building. Last year four blocks of his stuff burnt up, the damned old tinderboxes. 'It don't do me no good anyway,' he says. 'I couldn't get no insurance on them.' The papers says, '$500,000 Fire at the Beach,' but he couldn't get five cents for them buildings."

"Why does he keep the place open if he doesn't want any customers?" my girl asked.

"So he can lose money and take it off his income tax," Murph told her. "And now for God's sake don't order no pie à la mode like the last time, for I have to walk down to one end of the old shack for the pie and then I have to walk to the other end to the icehouse for the ice cream. Before you can get an order together in this place, you got to get a letter from the Pope. And then before you can find a dish to serve it in, you got to go through all that heap of old tinware, like a junkshop."

My girl meekly ordered watermelon, but Murph did not start to get it. He felt like talking.

"Before his wife died sixteen years ago, it wasn't so bad," he said. "Sometimes she would buy a round of drinks for the house. She was always soused. Twenty-four seasons I've worked here, God help me, and now it's too late to get fired. He'll die next winter surely."

He did.

A. J. LIEBLING was a reporter. Much of what he reported was funny, however, and he took a genial view of what was not funny. So he is not out of place in the company of humorists.

A. for Abbott J. for Joseph Liebling was born in New York City in 1904. His father, he said, "early introduced me to . . . the racecourse and the baseball park." After graduating from Dartmouth and the Columbia School of Journalism, he worked eight months for *The New York Times,* from which he was fired. Subsequently he worked as a reporter in Providence and as a reporter and feature writer on the New York *World Telegram.* In 1935 he joined the staff of *The New Yorker,* and helped to give that magazine a reputation for excellent reporting. From 1939 to 1944 he was its war correspondent in France, England, and North Africa. He contributed to the magazine until his death in 1963.

Liebling loved good food, a passion signalled by his large stomach and his tendency to report about places in terms of what he got to eat in them. During World War II he wrote from Paris on the subject of army K rations: "flat waxed-cardboard packages —thirty-six to a case—each containing the ready-to-eat components of a nourishing, harmless, and gastronomically despicable meal. . . . (Among troops actively engaged, a K ration beat nothing to eat, but it was a photo finish.) " Liebling's Normandy was the only place to get an *araignée,* a spidery-looking water crab: "The

Norman cook has . . . made a discreet incision around the periphery of the carapace, permitting the spider-eater, after he has sufficiently admired his specimen, to lift the top like a lid and attack the white interior from above." When Liebling told *The New Yorker*'s editor, Harold Ross, that he wanted to travel in the Midwest and write about it, Ross glared at him: "You wouldn't like it, Liebling. You wouldn't like it." Ross was right. Later Liebling contemptuously described the region as a place where a salad is something with marshmallows in it.

Liebling's other passions were the sports world and the newspapers. He was an exacting observer of both. After one boxing match, he wrote: "Some of the reporters, describing the blow in the morning papers, called it a 'sneak punch,' which is journalese for one the reporter didn't see but technically means a lead thrown before the other man has warmed up or while he is musing about the gate receipts." Some of Liebling's writing on World War II, boxing, food, newspapers, and other matters are collected in *The Most of A. J. Liebling*.

"The only way to write," Liebling once said, "is well. How is nobody's business but your own."

JOHN LARDNER

Death of a Simian and Scholar

As fine an ape as I knew was Gargantua, the circus star, who passed from this footstool a couple of weeks ago. He is gone but not forgotten. I have postponed my private obituary of this congenial gorilla until I was absolutely sure he was dead. An airplane transporting his remains lost 1,000 feet of altitude when the pilot heard a thumping noise amidships. It turned out to be a loose crate or a gremlin or something, not Gargy come to life.

Although we were acquainted socially, it was my business relationship with the noted entertainer that I valued most highly. In association with Mr. Gene Tunney, a gifted performer in his own right in a lower weight division, I once tried to promote a match of skill and strength between

Gargantua and Tony Galento, the spheroid barkeep of Orange, New Jersey. Had Galento not declined the test, we would all have cleaned up.

As it was, the thing fell through, and the four of us went our separate ways. Tunney became a uranium miner. Gargantua has gone to his reward. Galento is a wrestler, and your correspondent changes ribbons on typewriters. It is useless to sit around and speculate on what might have been.

Gargantua was an up-and-coming young ape of about five years, beginning to make his presence felt in show business, when he caught the eye of Mr. Tunney. Tunney was then sports editor of a paper called the *Connecticut Nutmeg*. As an editor, he thought he had to take a stand. So he took a stand against Gargantua. "Gorillas are overrated" was the editorial policy of Mr. Tunney.

That, of course, was directly opposed to the policy of another editor, the late Arthur Brisbane, who thought a gorilla could lick any five human beings. Reaching for his *Encyclopaedia Britannica,* Mr. Tunney made some rapid notes and announced that any third-rate heavyweight fighter could lick Gargantua. When your correspondent proposed Galento, a third-rate heavyweight second to none, as a worthy contender, Mr. Tunney leaped at the idea. So I went around to contact the rival camps.

Now it happened that Mr. Tunney had misread his *Britannica* or got hold of an early edition with incomplete returns. He thought it said that a gorilla has thirteen ribs, as against twenty-four for a human being or an Orange, New Jersey, barkeeper. What a gorilla really has is thirteen pairs of ribs, making twenty-six in all.

"Tunney is being ridiculous," said Gargantua's manager, a Mr. Dick Kroener, whom I found moodily biting his fingernails while Gargantua did roadwork around the inside of his cage. "It never pays to knock gorillas. My principal, here, can make shredded wheat out of the likes of Galento."

Galento's manager, Mr. Joe (Yussel the Muscle) Jacobs, seemed to share that suspicion, though he put it in another way.

"Let Tunney fight the ape. I will carry the bucket for him," said Mr. Jacobs coldly. "My tiger fights nobody but humans and such. Besides, our engagement book is full up. Ain't it, Anthony?"

"Right to the ears," agreed Mr. Galento. "I would like to belt over this circus bum, but I got no time."

Soon afterward a rumor began to circulate in the prizefight business that Mr. Tunney had deliberately misrepresented the number of Gargantua's ribs in order to lure Galento into the ring with the crowd-pleasing African. Now, since I know that Mr. Tunney was prepared to bet handsomely on Galento, that he is the soul of honor, and that he still thinks gorillas are overrated, I am certain that no such stratagem was in his thoughts. If ever a chap believed in the cause of man over monkey, it is this same Tunney.

However, I am forced to disagree with him. I saw a good deal of Gargantua between that time and the time of his death. We had little to say to each other, both being of a reserved, introspective turn of mind, but whenever I watched him tear an automobile tire in two, I mused on the folly of man and his vaulting ambitions. So, no doubt, did Gargantua. May he walk in green pastures.

JOHN LARDNER was one of Ring Lardner's four sons, and an excellent and funny writer in his own right. He was born in Chicago in 1912. He graduated from Phillips Academy in Andover, Massachusetts, in 1929, and attended Harvard for a year. In 1931 he started as a reporter on the New York *Herald Tribune*. Later he became a columnist on *Newsweek* and a critic and reviewer on *The New Yorker*. In 1942 he began serving as a war correspondent for both magazines, moving with the U.S. Army from North Africa to Italy to Iwo Jima and Okinawa.

Lardner took a scientific interest in sports-world lore and wrote frequently about boxing. He was also fascinated by the details of popular culture, and wrote either sympathetically or bitingly—according to the subject's merits—of popular good-guys like Gargantua and popular bad-guys like radio and TV interviewers. He was particularly hard on the latter for their muddled use of the English language; he himself had a reporter's respect for plain talking and for facts.

Lardner died in 1969. Many of his best pieces are collected in *The World of John Lardner*.

MARIO PUZO

Davie Shaw's Friends

The following selection first appeared as two chapters in Mr.
Puzo's novel for children, "The Runaway Summer of Davie
Shaw." DavieShaw ("that is how everybody pronounced his
name, all run together") here begins the fourth leg of a cross-
country trip with his pony, Mustang. Destination: New York City,
where he plans to surprise his parents by meeting them at the end
of their round-the-world vacation.

That afternoon DavieShaw passed a road sign that said NEW
YORK 1500 MILES. Then he saw another sign with an
arrow that said THIS WAY TO THE EXACT MIDDLE
OF THE UNITED STATES. He thought that was so interesting he followed the arrow signs on to a side road. Mustang
followed him very slowly. After a little while they came to a
mansion surrounded by signs that read: THIS HOUSE
RESTS ON THE EXACT MIDDLE OF THE UNITED

STATES *Lat 39 degrees 50′ N Long 98 degrees 35′ W*
SMITH COUNTY, KANSAS.

A middle-aged man was coming out of the house carrying two suitcases. He noticed Davie watching and said,
"Hello there young feller. Do you want to see the exact, exact
center of the United States?"

"Yes sir," Davie said.

"Then come into the house," the man said.

He led Davie into the living room. There was a little
table with a stand that held the American flag. On the table
was a sign which read THIS IS THE EXACT MIDDLE OF
THE USA.

DavieShaw felt very excited. But then he noticed that
the middle-aged man was sitting on the sofa crying.

"What's the matter?" Davie asked.

"It's not true any more," the man said. "That's why I'm
going away. It used to be true, but now that Alaska and
Hawaii are new states, of course the center changes. And now
no one comes in here any more. They are going to take down
all the signs and I won't be famous any more. And I was
really so happy. I never envied whoever it was that lived in
the exact center of North America or who lived in the exact
center of the world. But now I don't have anything, and so
I'm going to move away."

Davie felt sorry for this man. He said, "I have a pony
who carries suitcases and bundles. Do you want him to carry
your things too?"

"You're very kind," the man said. "I don't even know
where I'm going. Maybe I'll just go along with you for a
while. Will that be all right?"

"Sure," DavieShaw said. So they left the house and filled the pony cart with the man's suitcases.

Then DavieShaw told Mustang to "Let's go." As soon as the pony started moving, the man hopped into the pony cart. Mustang stopped. Then DavieShaw had to explain that Mustang would never carry anyone who could walk on his own two feet.

"Aha," said the man, "no free rides, eh?"

"I guess that's how Mustang feels," DavieShaw said.

They walked all that day along the highway. Once the man said, "You know, if you sold the pony you could hitchhike to New York faster than we can walk." But Davie didn't pay attention. That was silly.

The man's name was Harry Hobbs, and he wasn't very good company. He even admitted it to Davie.

"I'm not very good company," he said. "People who are having troubles are usually not. That's why other people snub them. It's not that people are unkind, you know. People are helpful to people in trouble. But they don't want to be with them because they are not very good company."

"Is it that important to be very good company?" Davie asked.

"Oh, I assure you that it is," Harry Hobbs said. "I've known men who were not honest, not brave, not trustworthy, not truth-tellers. And everything was forgiven them because they were such good company."

"I don't think that is fair," DavieShaw said.

"Of course it isn't," Harry Hobbs said. "Who said that it was?"

Night was falling when they saw a huge house off to the side of the road. They decided to ask permission to sleep there. So they knocked on the door. When it opened, they were surprised to see a man dressed in a tuxedo and top hat as if he were going to a fancy-dress ball.

They explained what they wished, and this handsome gentleman said, "Certainly, certainly, you have picked the best possible house to sleep in. But first have a little supper."

When they had finished eating, the host led them into a huge living room that had a lot of armchairs and large oil paintings of famous men like Napoleon and George Washington on the walls. Davie was surprised to see that there were five other men there, all dressed up in very nice clothes as if they were going to the theater or around the world.

Harry Hobbs was also astonished and asked, "Is there going to be a party this evening?"

"Oh no," said the host. "They just come here to sleep. They are part of my cult, or my circle. We all believe in one thing. I shall introduce them to you as a group under the heading of what we believe in.

"I am a writer," said the host, "and these other gentlemen also have high aspirations. Going from left to right, our left to right of course, not their left to right, is a painter, a sculptor, a daring auto racer, an explorer, and that young fellow there is a baseball player who is waiting to play center field for the Yankees.

"Now you may wonder," said the host, "why we are all here in this lonely house not doing anything. Let me explain. I used to get all upset trying to write my books. I would sit down and just couldn't write. Days went by, years went by and still nothing happened. When I talked about my plans, people used to laugh at me. They just didn't realize how hard it is to do something. Then I met my friend the painter. He had the same trouble. But it was very nice to talk about the work we were going to do that would make us rich and famous. Then I met the sculptor, and he really had more trouble than all of us. Do you know how much it costs to get a big block of marble and how your muscles hurt if you have to chip at it all day and try to make it into a face? And then we met the daring auto racer, but he hasn't got his driver's license yet. And of course the baseball player has to practice every day, doing the same thing over and over again. The explorer can't stand the cold and he can't stand the heat. This house has air conditioning and a central furnace and he loves to live here.

"Now in all the newspapers, you often read about how an artist wakes up one morning to find himself rich and famous, just like that. It happened to Ernest Hemingway. It happened to Mickey Mantle, it happened to Stanley and Livingston. Nobody knew them and suddenly one morning they woke up and just like that, they were rich and famous. And then we realized, *that's what everybody wants.* It's no fun working hard and being rejected and worrying about how your paintings or your explorings will come out. So we all decided to stick together in my house and talk about our writings and sculptings, and one morning it will happen to us. We'll wake up and be rich and famous."

"But why are you all dressed up?" DavieShaw asked.

"Well, now," said the host. "We wouldn't want to wake up rich and famous in our everyday clothes, would we?"

For the first time DavieShaw was almost rude and scornful to his elders.

"That is the silliest thing I've ever heard," he said sternly.

"Oh no. Oh no. Oh no," Harold Hobbs said excitedly. "It happened to me already. I always wanted to be rich and famous, too. I lived all alone in my little house and nobody ever paid any attention to me. I wanted to be rich and famous but I never had the time to work at it, and I was waiting for the right moment. Then one day truckloads of engineers came with surveying equipment and ran all around. I watched them from my porch. I even turned off the radio. And do you know, they found out that my house was the exact center of the forty-eight states of the United States of America. The next morning it was in all the papers. Everybody came from all over to see the exact center of the United States, and I charged admission fees to the living room. That's where it was. I put up a special table with a special flag and I sold souvenirs. I really worked at it then. And do you know, when you become rich and famous you can work better. It's not so hard. I mean if you're already rich and famous it's much easier to become rich and famous in other things. I sang in vaudeville, I gave lectures to high schools, I was even elected mayor. It all happened to me just as these gentlemen think it will happen."

The host in his tuxedo and all the other men crowded around Harry Hobbs to shake his hand and beg him to stay with them. When he told them how the addition of Alaska and Hawaii had made him lose his fame and riches, they all patted him on the shoulder and said, "If it happened once it will happen again."

Why they said this, DavieShaw didn't know, because it obviously was not true. A lot of things happened just once and never happened again.

They all begged DavieShaw to stay with them, but Davie

was too responsible. He knew that if he didn't walk to New York City he would never get there. But Harold Hobbs stayed, and so the next morning DavieShaw left with his pony, Mustang. To tell the truth he was not sorry about losing Harry Hobbs. He was a nice man and DavieShaw felt sorry for him, but he was really not very good company.

MARIO PUZO is mainly a novelist, not a humorist. This profession, however, does not keep him from being funny. The characters in his novels speak like real people, which means that they sound funny a good part of the time. And like A. J. Liebling's serious reporting, Mr. Puzo's serious novels reflect a view of life that is basically humorous: Both writers are quick to point out human idiocy, and just as quick to be tolerant and good-natured about it.

However, Mr. Puzo has written one truly comic book, from which the selection here is taken—a novel for children, *The Runaway Summer of Davie Shaw*. By writing it, Mr. Puzo joined those very few writers (E. B. White, the author of *Stuart Little*, is one of them) whose books can be laughed at by adults as well as children.

Mario Puzo was born in New York City in 1920. He served in the infantry in World War II, and he spent some time in Germany after the war. Then he returned to New York, where he studied literature and writing at Columbia University and at the New School for Social Research. For many years he worked as a magazine writer and editor. Now he works on his own: studying the Las Vegas gambling tables to get material for a magazine article; panning the new novels by rival writers; and working on his latest book in his peaceful Long Island home, surrounded by his wife and five children. Mr. Puzo is the author of three novels: *The Dark Arena, The Fortunate Pilgrim,* and *The Godfather*.

Unlike Harry Hobbs, Mr. Puzo is excellent company.

NOEL COWARD

Hands Across the Sea

Reading a play is nothing like seeing one. In a comedy, especially, an actor can make something funny that isn't at all funny on paper. Nevertheless, Noel Coward's comedies read funnier than most, because he writes witty lines. The main thing that is missing in reading "Hands Across the Sea" is pace. Mr. Coward directed his plays, and acted in them, at almost breakneck speed. "Hands Across the Sea" is best read very fast.

The action of the play takes place in the drawing-room of the GILPINS' *flat in London.*

Time: Present Day.

The Scene is the drawing-room of the GILPINS' *flat in London. The room is nicely furnished and rather untidy. There is a portable gramophone on one small table and a tray of cocktail things on another; apart from these, the furnishing can be left to the discretion of the producer.*

When the curtain rises the telephone is ringing. WAL-
TERS, *a neat parlourmaid, enters and answers it. The
time is about six p.m.*

WALTERS (*at telephone*) : Hallo—yes—no, her ladyship's
not back yet—she said she'd be in at five, so she ought to be
here at any minute now—what name, please?—Rawlingson—
Mr. and Mrs. Rawlingson—— (*She scribbles on the pad.*)
Yes—I'll tell her——

> *She hangs up the receiver and goes out. There is the
> sound of voices in the hall and* LADY MAUREEN GILPIN
> *enters, followed at a more leisurely pace by her husband,*
> PETER GILPIN. MAUREEN, *nicknamed* PIGGIE *by her inti-
> mates, is a smart, attractive woman in the thirties.* PETER
> *is tall and sunburned and reeks of the Navy.*

PIGGIE (*as she comes in*) : —and you can send the car
back for me at eleven-thirty—it's quite simple, darling, I wish
you wouldn't be so awfully complicated about everything——

PETER: What happens if my damned dinner goes on
longer than that and I get stuck?

PIGGIE: You just get stuck, darling, and then you get
unstuck and get a taxi——

PETER (*grumbling*) : I shall be in uniform, clinking
with medals——

PIGGIE: If you take my advice you'll faint dead away at
eleven o'clock and then you can come home in the car and
change and have time for everything——

PETER: I can't faint dead away under the nose of the C.-
in-C.

PIGGIE: You can feel a little poorly, can't you—anybody

has the right to feel a little poorly—— *(She sees the telephone pad.)* My God!

PETER: What is it?

PIGGIE: The Rawlingsons.

PETER: Who the hell are they?

PIGGIE: I'd forgotten all about them—I must get Maud at once—— *(She sits at the telephone and dials a number.)*

PETER: Who are the Rawlingsons?

PIGGIE: Maud and I stayed with them in Samolo, I told you about it, that time when we had to make a forced landing—they practically saved our lives—— *(At telephone.)* Hullo—Maud—darling, the Rawlingsons are on us—what—the RAWLINGSONS—yes—I asked them to-day and forgot all about it—you must come at once—but, darling, you *must*— Oh, dear—no, no, that was the Frobishers, these are the ones we stayed with—mother and father and daughter—you must remember—pretty girl with bad legs—— No—they didn't have a son—we swore we'd give them a lovely time when they came home on leave—I know they didn't have a son, that was those other people in Penang—— Oh, all right—you'll have to do something about them, though—let me ask them to lunch with you to-morrow—all right—one-thirty—I'll tell them—— *(She hangs up.)* —she can't come——

PETER: You might have warned me that a lot of Colonial strangers were coming trumpeting into the house——

PIGGIE: I tell you I'd forgotten——

PETER: That world trip was a grave mistake——

PIGGIE: Who can I get that's celebrated—to give them a thrill?

PETER: Why do they have to have a thrill?

PIGGIE: I'll get Clare, anyway—— (*She dials another number.*)

PETER: She'll frighten them to death.

PIGGIE: Couldn't you change early and come in your uniform? That would be better than nothing——

PETER: Perhaps they'd like to watch me having my bath!

PIGGIE (*at telephone*): I want to speak to Mrs. Wedderburn, please—yes—— (*To* PETER.) I do wish you'd be a little helpful—— (*At telephone.*) Clare?—this is Piggie—I want you to come round at once and help me with the Rawlingsons—no, I know you haven't, but that doesn't matter—— Mother, father and daughter—very sweet—they were divine to us in the East—I'm repaying hospitality—Maud's having them to lunch to-morrow and Peter's going to take them round the dockyard——

PETER: I'm not going to do any such thing——

PIGGIE: Shut up, I just thought of that and it's a *very* good idea—— (*At telephone.*) All right, darling—as soon as you can—— (*She hangs up.*) —I must go and change——

PETER: You know perfectly well I haven't time to take mothers and fathers and daughters with bad legs round the dockyard——

PIGGIE: It wouldn't take a minute, they took us all over their rubber plantation.

PETER: It probably served you right.

PIGGIE: You're so disobliging, darling, you really should try to conquer it—it's something to do with being English, I think—as a race I'm ashamed of us—no sense of hospitality— the least we can do when people are kind to us in far-off places is to be a little gracious in return.

PETER: They weren't kind to me in far-off places.

PIGGIE: You know there's a certain grudging, sullen streak in your character—I've been very worried about it lately—it's spreading like a forest fire——

PETER: Why don't you have them down for the week-end?

PIGGIE: Don't be so idiotic, how can I possibly? There's no room to start with and even if there were they'd be utterly wretched——

PETER: I don't see why.

PIGGIE: They wouldn't know anybody—they probably wouldn't have the right clothes—they'd keep on huddling about in uneasy little groups——

PETER: The amount of uneasy little groups that three people can huddle about in is negligible.

ALASTAIR CORBETT *saunters into the room. He is good-looking and also distinctly Naval in tone.*

ALLY: Hallo, chaps.

PIGGIE: Ally, darling—how lovely—we're in trouble— Peter'll tell you all about it——

The telephone rings and she goes to it. The following conversations occur simultaneously.

ALLY: What trouble?

PETER: More of Piggie's beach friends.

ALLY: Let's have a drink.

PETER: Cocktail?

ALLY: No, a long one, whisky and soda.

PETER (*going to drink table*) : All right.

ALLY: What beach friends?

PETER: People Maud and Piggie picked up in the East.

PIGGIE (*at phone*) : Hullo!—Yes—Robert, dear—how lovely! (*To others.*) It's Robert.

ALLY: Piggie ought to stay at home more.

PIGGIE (*on phone*) : Where are you?

PETER: That's what I say!

PIGGIE (*on phone*) : Oh, what a shame!—No—Peter's going to sea on Thursday—I'm going down on Saturday.

ALLY: Rubber, I expect—everybody in the East's rubber.

PIGGIE (*on phone*) : No—nobody particular—just Clare and Bogey and I think Pops; but he thinks he's got an ulcer or something and might not be able to come.

PETER: We thought you might be a real friend and take them over the dockyard.

ALLY: What on earth for?

PETER: Give them a thrill.

PIGGIE (*on phone*) : All right—I'll expect you—no, I don't think it can be a very big one—he looks as bright as a button.

ALLY: Why don't you take them over the dockyard?

PETER: I shall be at sea, Thursday onwards—exercises!

PIGGIE (*on phone*) : No, darling, what is the use of having her—she only depresses you—oh—all right! (*Hangs up.*) Oh, dear——

PETER: It's quite easy for you—you can give them lunch on board.

ALLY: We're in dry dock.

PETER: They won't mind. (*To* PIGGIE.) What is it?

PIGGIE: Robert—plunged in gloom—he's got to do a course at Greenwich—he ran into a tram in Devonport—and he's had a row with Molly—he wants me to have her for the week-end so they can make it up all over everybody. Have you told Ally about the Rawlingsons?

PETER: Yes, he's taking them over the dockyard, lunching them on board and then he's going to show them a submarine——

PIGGIE: Marvellous! You're an angel, Ally—I must take off these clothes, I'm going mad——

She goes out of the room at a run.

There is the sound of the front-door bell.

PETER: Let's go into my room—I can show you the plans——

ALLY: Already? They've been pretty quick with them.

PETER: I made a few alterations—there wasn't enough deck space—she ought to be ready by October, I shall have her sent straight out to Malta——

ALLY: Come on, we shall be caught——

They go off on the left as WALTERS *ushers in* MR. *and* MRS. WADHURST *on the right.*

The WADHURSTS *are pleasant, middle-aged people, their manner is a trifle timorous.*

WALTERS: Her ladyship is changing, I'll tell her you are here.

MRS. WADHURST: Thank you.

MR. WADHURST: Thank you very much.

WALTERS *goes out.*

The WADHURSTS *look round the room.*

MRS. WADHURST: It's a very nice flat.

MR. WADHURST: Yes—yes, it is.

MRS. WADHURST (*scrutinizing a photograph*): That must be him.

MR. WADHURST: Who?

MRS. WADHURST: The Commander.

MR. WADHURST: Yes—I expect it is.

Mrs. Wadhurst: Sailors always have such nice open faces, don't they?

Mr. Wadhurst: Yes, I suppose so.

Mrs. Wadhurst: Clean-cut and look you straight in the eye—I like men who look you straight in the eye.

Mr. Wadhurst: Yes, it's very nice.

Mrs. Wadhurst (*at another photograph*) : This must be her sister—I recognize her from the *Tatler*—look—she was Lady Hurstley, you know, then she was Lady Macfadden and I don't know who she is now.

Mr. Wadhurst: Neither do I.

Mrs. Wadhurst: What a dear little boy—such a sturdy little fellow—look at the way he's holding his engine.

Mr. Wadhurst: Is that his engine?

Mrs. Wadhurst: He has rather a look of Donald Hotchkiss, don't you think?

Mr. Wadhurst: Yes, dear.

Mrs. Wadhurst: I must say they have very nice things— oh, dear, how lovely to be well off—I must write to the Brostows by the next mail and tell them all about it.

Mr. Wadhurst: Yes, you must.

Mrs. Wadhurst: Don't you think we'd better sit down?

Mr. Wadhurst: Why not?

Mrs. Wadhurst: You sit in that chair and I'll sit on the sofa.

She sits on the sofa. He sits on the chair.

Mr. Wadhurst: Yes, dear.

Mrs. Wadhurst: I wish you wouldn't look quite so uncomfortable, Fred, there's nothing to be uncomfortable about.

Mr. Wadhurst: She does expect us, doesn't she?

MRS. WADHURST: Of course, I talked to her myself on the telephone last Wednesday, she was perfectly charming and said that we were to come without fail and that it would be divine.

MR. WADHURST: I still feel we should have telephoned again just to remind her. People are always awfully busy in London.

MRS. WADHURST: I do hope Lady Dalborough will be here, too—I should like to see her again—she was so nice.

MR. WADHURST: She was the other one, wasn't she?

MRS. WADHURST (*irritably*) : What do you mean, the other one?

MR. WADHURST: I mean not this one.

MRS. WADHURST: She's the niece of the Duke of Frensham, her mother was Lady Merrit, she was a great traveller too—I believe she went right across the Sahara dressed as an Arab. In those days that was a very dangerous thing to do.

MR. WADHURST: I shouldn't think it was any too safe now.

WALTERS *enters and ushers in* MR. BURNHAM, *a nondescript young man carrying a longish roll of cardboard.*

WALTERS: I'll tell the Commander you're here.

MR. BURNHAM: Thanks—thanks very much.

WALTERS *goes out.*

MRS. WADHURST (*after a slightly awkward silence*) : How do you do?

MR. BURNHAM: How do you do?

MRS. WADHURST (*with poise*) : This is my husband.

MR. BURNHAM: How do you do?

MR. WADHURST: How do you do?

They shake hands.

Mrs. Wadhurst (*vivaciously*) : Isn't this a charming room—so—so lived in.

Mr. Burnham: Yes.

Mr. Wadhurst: Are you in the Navy, too?

Mr. Burnham: No.

Mrs. Wadhurst (*persevering*) : It's so nice to be home again—we come from Malaya, you know.

Mr. Burnham: Oh—Malaya.

Mrs. Wadhurst: Yes, Lady Maureen and Lady Dalborough visited us there—my husband has a rubber plantation up-country—there's been a terrible slump, of course, but we're trying to keep our heads above water—aren't we, Fred?

Mr. Wadhurst: Yes, dear, we certainly are.

Mrs. Wadhurst: Have you ever been to the East?

Mr. Burnham: No.

Mrs. Wadhurst: It's very interesting really, although the climate's rather trying until you get used to it, and of course the one thing we do miss is the theatre——

Mr. Burnham: Yes—of course.

Mrs. Wadhurst: There's nothing my husband and I enjoy so much as a good play, is there, Fred?

Mr. Wadhurst: Nothing.

Mrs. Wadhurst: And all we get is films, and they're generally pretty old by the time they come out to us—— (*She laughs gaily.*)

Mr. Wadhurst: Do you go to the theatre much?

Mr. Burnham: No.

There is silence which is broken by the telephone ringing. Everybody jumps.

MRS. WADHURST: Oh, dear—do you think we ought to answer it?

MR. WADHURST: I don't know.

The telephone continues to ring. CLARE WEDDER-BURN *comes in. She is middle-aged, well-dressed and rather gruff. She is followed by* "BOGEY" GOSLING, *a Major in the Marines, a good-looking man in the thirties.*

CLARE: Hallo—where's the old girl?

MRS. WADHURST (*nervously*) : I—er, I'm afraid I——

CLARE (*going to the telephone*) : Mix a cocktail, Bogey —I'm a stretcher case—— (*At telephone.*) Hallo—no, it's me—Clare—— God knows, dear—shall I tell her to call you back?—all right—no, it was bloody, darling—a gloomy dinner at the Embassy, then the worst play I've ever sat through and then the Café de Paris and that awful man who does things with a duck—I've already seen him six times, darling—oh, you know, he pinches its behind and it quacks 'Land of Hope and Glory'—I don't know whether it hurts it or not—I minded at first but I'm past caring now, after all, it's not like perform-ing dogs, I mind about the performing dogs terribly—all right—good-bye—— (*She hangs up and turns to* MRS. WAD-HURST.) Ducks are pretty bloody anyway, don't you think?

MRS. WADHURST: I don't know very much about them.

CLARE: The man swears it's genuine talent, but I think it's the little nip that does it.

MRS. WADHURST: It sounds rather cruel.

CLARE: It's a gloomy form of entertainment anyhow, particularly as I've always hated 'Land of Hope and Glory'——

BOGEY: Cocktail?

CLARE (*taking off her hat*) : Thank God!

BOGEY *hands round cocktails, the* WADHURSTS *and* MR. BURNHAM *accept them and sip them in silence.*

BOGEY: I suppose Piggie's in the bath.

CLARE: Go and rout her out.

BOGEY: Wait till I've had a drink.

CLARE (*to* MRS. WADHURST) : Is Peter home or is he still darting about the Solent?

MRS WADHURST: I'm afraid I couldn't say—you see——

BOGEY: I saw him last night with Janet——

CLARE: Hasn't she had her baby yet?

BOGEY: She hadn't last night.

CLARE: That damned baby's been hanging over us all for months——

*The telephone rings—*CLARE *answers it.*

(*At telephone.*) Hallo—yes—hallo, darling—no, it's Clare— yes, he's here—— No, I really couldn't face it—yes, if I were likely to go to India I'd come, but I'm not likely to go to India—— I think Rajahs bumble up a house-party so ter- ribly—yes, I know *he's* different, but the other one's awful— Angela had an agonizing time with him—all the the dining- room chairs had to be changed because they were leather and his religion prevented him sitting on them—all the dogs had to be kept out of the house because they were unclean, which God knows was true of the Bedlington, but the other ones were clean as whistles—and then to round everything off he took Laura Merstham in his car and made passes at her all the way to Newmarket—all right, darling—here he is—— (*To* BOGEY.) It's Nina, she wants to talk to you——

She hands the telephone to BOGEY, *who reaches for it and lifts the wire so that it just misses* MRS. WAD-

HURST'S *hat. It isn't quite long enough so he has to bend down to speak with his face practically touching her.*

BOGEY (*at telephone*): Hallo, Nin—— I can't on Wednesday, I've got a Guest Night—it's a hell of a long way, it'd take hours——

PIGGIE *comes in with a rush.*

PIGGIE: I am so sorry——

CLARE: Shhh!

BOGEY: Shut up, I can't hear——

PIGGIE (*in a shrill whisper*): Who is it?

CLARE: Nina.

BOGEY (*at telephone*): Well, you can tell George to leave it for me—and I can pick it up.

PIGGIE: How lovely to see you again!

BOGEY (*at telephone*): No, I shan't be leaving till about ten, so if he leaves it by nine-thirty I'll get it all right——

PIGGIE: My husband will be here in a minute—he has to go to sea on Thursday, but he's arranged for you to be taken over the dockyard at Portsmouth——

BOGEY (*at telephone*): Give the old boy a crack on the jaw.

PIGGIE: It's the most thrilling thing in the world. You see how the torpedoes are made—millions of little wheels inside, all clicking away like mad—and they cost thousands of pounds each——

BOGEY (*at telephone*): No, I saw her last night—not yet, but at any moment now—I should think—— All right—— Call me at Chatham—if I can get away I shall have to bring Mickie, too——

PIGGIE: How much do torpedoes cost each, Clare?

CLARE: God knows, darling—something fantastic—ask Bogey——

PIGGIE: Bogey——

BOGEY: What?

PIGGIE: How much do torpedoes cost each?

BOGEY: What?— (*at telephone*) —wait a minute, Piggie's yelling at me——

PIGGIE: Torpedoes—— (*She makes a descriptive gesture.*)

BOGEY: Oh, thousands and thousands—terribly expensive things—ask Peter—— (*At telephone*) —If I do bring him you'll have to be frightfully nice to him, he's been on the verge of suicide for weeks——

PIGGIE: Don't let her go, I must talk to her——

BOGEY (*at telephone*) : Hold on a minute, Piggie wants to talk to you—all right—I'll let you know—here she is——

PIGGIE *leans over the sofa and takes the telephone from* BOGEY, *who steps over the wire and stumbles over* MRS. WADHURST.

BOGEY: I'm most awfully sorry——

MRS. WADHURST: Not at all——

PIGGIE (*to* MRS. WADHURST) : It's so lovely you being in England—— (*At telephone.*) Darling—what was the meaning of that sinister little invitation you sent me?

BOGEY: You know what Mickey is.

PIGGIE (*at telephone*) : No, dear, I really can't—I always get so agitated——

CLARE: Why does he go on like that? It's so tiresome.

PIGGIE (*at telephone*) : I'll come if Clare will—— (*To* CLARE.) Are you going to Nina's Indian ding-dong?

CLARE: Not without an anæsthetic.

Piggie (*at telephone*): She's moaning a bit, but I'll persuade her—what happens after dinner?—the man with the duck from the Café de Paris—— (*To the room in general.*) She's got that sweet duck from the Café de Paris——

Clare: Give me another cocktail, Bogey, I want to get so drunk that I just can't hear any more——

Piggie (*at telephone*): But, darling, do you think it's quite *wise*—I mean Maharajahs are terribly touchy and there's probably something in their religion about ducks being mortal sin or something—you know how difficult they are about cows and pigs—just a minute—(*To the* Wadhursts.) You can tell us, of course——

Mr. Wadhurst: I beg your pardon?

Piggie: Do Indians mind ducks?

Mr. Wadhurst: I—I don't think so——

Bogey: Do you come from India?

Mrs. Wadhurst: No, Malaya.

Piggie: It's the same sort of thing, though, isn't it?—if they don't mind them in Malaya it's unlikely that they'd mind them in India—— (*At telephone.*) It'll probably be all right, but you'd better get Douglas Byng as a standby.

Clare: There might be something in their religion about Douglas Byng.

Piggie: Shh! (*At telephone.*) Everyone's making such a noise! The room's full of the most frightful people. Darling, it definitely *is* Waterloo Station—— No, I'm almost sure he can't—he's going to sea on Thursday—don't be silly, dear, you can't be in the Navy without going to sea *sometimes*——

Peter *enters, followed by* Ally.

(*At telephone.*) Here he is now, you can ask him your-self—— (*To* Peter.) Peter, it's Nina, she wants to talk to you—— (*To the* WADHURSTS.) This is my husband and Commander Corbett—he's been longing to meet you and thank you for being so sweet to us—I told him all about your heavenly house and the plantation——

MRS. WADHURST (*bridling—to* ALLY) : It was most delightful, I assure you, to have Lady Maureen with us——

PIGGIE: Not him, him—that's the wrong one——

MRS. WADHURST: Oh, I'm so sorry——

PETER (*shaking hands with* MRS. WADHURST) : It was so kind of you—my wife has talked of nothing else——

PIGGIE (*grabbing him*) : Here—Nina's yelling like a banshee——

PETER: Excuse me. (*He takes the telephone.*) Hallo, Nin—what for?—— No, I can't, but Piggie probably can—— (*To* PIGGIE.) Can you go to Nina's party for the Rajahs?

PIGGIE: We've been through all that——

PETER: All right—I didn't know—— (*At telephone.*) No, I shall be at sea for about three days—it isn't tiresome at all, I like it——

PIGGIE (*to* MRS. WADHURST) : How's your daughter?

MRS. WADHURST (*surprised*) : She's a little better, thank you.

PIGGIE: Oh, has she been ill? I'm so sorry.

MR. WADHURST (*gently*) : She's been ill for five years.

PIGGIE (*puzzled*) : How dreadful for you—are you happy with that cocktail, or would you rather have tea?

MRS. WADHURST: This is delicious, thank you.

PETER (*at telephone*) : I honestly can't do anything about that, Nina, you might be able to find out from the Admiral—well, if his mother was mad too that is an extenuating circumstance—he'll probably be sent home—— (*To*

CLARE.) Did you know that Freda Bathurst had once been in an asylum?

CLARE: No, but it explains a lot.

PIGGIE: Why?

PETER: Her son went mad in Hong Kong.

CLARE: What did he do?

PETER: I don't know, but Nina's in a state about it.

PIGGIE: I don't see what it's got to do with Nina——

PETER: He's a relation of some sort—— (*At telephone.*) What did he do, Nina?—— Oh—— Oh, I see—— Oh—well, he'll certainly be sent home and a good job too, we can't have that sort of thing in the Service—— If I were you I'd keep well out of it—all right—— Good-bye. (*He hangs up.*)

PIGGIE: What was it?

PETER: I couldn't possibly tell you.

PIGGIE: Poor boy, I expect the climate had something to do with it—the climate's awful in Hong Kong—look at poor old Wally Smythe——

ALLY (*to the* WADHURSTS): Did you ever know Wally Smythe?

MRS. WADHURST: No, I'm afraid not.

CLARE: You didn't miss much.

PIGGIE: I adored Wally, he was a darling.

CLARE: He kept on having fights all the time—I do hate people hitting people—— (*To* MRS. WADHURST.) Don't you?

MRS. WADHURST: Yes.

> *There is suddenly complete silence*—PIGGIE *breaks it with an effort.*

PIGGIE (*vivaciously to the* WADHURSTS): Maud was so frightfully sorry that she couldn't come to-day—she's pining to see you again and she asked me to ask you if you'd lunch there to-morrow?

MRS. WADHURST: How very kind of her.

PIGGIE: She's got a divine little house hidden away in a mews, it's frightfully difficult to find—— (*The telephone rings.*) I've got millions of questions I want to ask you, what happened to that darling old native who did a dance with a sword?—— (*At telephone.*) Hallo—(*Continuing to everyone in general.*) It was the most exciting thing I've ever seen, all the villagers sat round in torchlight and they beat—— (*At telephone.*) Hallo—yes, speaking—— (*Continuing*) beat drums and the—— (*At telephone*) hallo—darling, I'd no idea you were back—— (*to everybody*) and the old man tore himself to shreds in the middle, it was marvellous—— (*At telephone.*) I can't believe it, where are you speaking from?—— My dear, you're *not!*—— (*To everybody.*) It's Boodie, she's got back last night and she's staying with Norman——

CLARE: Is Phyllis there?

PIGGIE (*at telephone*): Is Phyllis there?—— She's away?—— (*To* CLARE.) She's away.

PETER (*to* MR. WADHURST): That's the best joke I ever heard.

CLARE: It's made my entire season that's all, it's just made it.

PIGGIE (*at telephone*): You'd better come and dine tonight—I'm on a diet, so there's only spinach, but we can talk—— Yes, she's here—absolutely worn out—we all are—— Oh yes, it was pretty grim, it started all right and everything was going beautifully when Vera arrived, unasked, my dear, and more determined than Hitler—of course there was the most awful scene—Alice flounced upstairs with tears cascading down her face and locked herself in the cook's bedroom—— Clare tried to save the situation by dragging Lady Borrowdale on to the terrace——

CLARE (*sibilantly*) : That was *afterwards!*——

PIGGIE (*at telephone*) : Anyhow hell broke loose—you can imagine—Janet was there, of course, and we were all worried about her—no, it hasn't arrived yet, but the odds are mounting—— (*To everybody.*) She hasn't had it yet, has she, Peter?

PETER: If she has it was born in the gramophone department at Harrods—I left her there at four-thirty——

PIGGIE (*at telephone*) : No, it's still what's known as on the way—I'll expect you about eight-thirty—I've got to do my feet and then I'm going to relax—all right—yes, she's here—— (*To* CLARE.) Here, Clare, she wants to talk to you——

CLARE *in order to reach the telephone comfortably has to kneel on the sofa.*

CLARE: Excuse me.

MRS. WADHURST: I'm so sorry.

CLARE (*at telephone*) : Darling—I'm dead with surprise——

PIGGIE (*to* MRS. WADHURST) : Now you must tell me some more——

MRS. WADHURST: Well, really, I don't——

CLARE: Shhh!—I can't hear a word—— (*At telephone.*) He what?—when?—— He must be raving——

PIGGIE (*in a harsh whisper*) : Have you still got that sweet dog?

MRS. WADHURST (*also whispering*) : Yes, we've still got Rudolph.

PIGGIE (*to everybody*) : Rudolph's an angel, I can never tell you how divine he was—he used to come in every morning with my breakfast tray and jump on to the bed——

MRS. WADHURST (*horrified*) : Oh, you never told me that, how very naughty of him—he's very seldom allowed in the house at all——

PIGGIE (*puzzled*) : But—but——

MR. WADHURST: Perhaps you're thinking of some other dog, Lady Maureen—Rudolph is a Great Dane——

PIGGIE (*bewildered*) : Oh, yes, of course, how idiotic of me——

CLARE (*at telephone*) : —Well, all I can say is she ought to be deported—you can't go about making scenes like that, it's so lacking in everything—all right, darling—call me in the morning—I've got a hairdresser in the afternoon, why don't you make an appointment at the same time?—lovely—— Good-bye. (*She hangs up.*)

PIGGIE: Do sit down, Clare, and stop climbing about over everybody. (*To* MRS. WADHURST.) You must forgive me—this is a mad-house—it's always like this—I can't think why——

CLARE (*in a whisper to* PETER, *having noticed* MR. BURNHAM*) : Why's that man got a roll of music, is he going to sing?

PETER (*also in a whisper*) : I don't know—he ought by rights to be a lovely girl of sixteen——

MRS. WADHURST: Have you been in London for the whole season?

PIGGIE: Yes, it's been absolutely frightful, but my hus-

band is getting leave soon, so we shall be able to pop off
somewhere——

ALLY (*to* MR. WADHURST) : I suppose you've never run
across a chap in Burma called Beckwith?

MR. WADHURST: No, I've never been to Burma.

ALLY: He's in rubber, too, I believe—or tea—he's very
amusing.

MRS. WADHURST (*to* PIGGIE) : We did hope you'd come
and lunch with us one day—but I expect you're terribly
busy——

PIGGIE: My dear, I'd worship it—— (*The telephone
rings.*) Oh really, this telephone never stops for one minute—— (*At telephone.*) Hallo—yes, speaking—— Who?—
Mrs. Rawlingson—— Oh, yes, yes, yes—— (*She hands the
telephone to* MRS. WADHURST.) Here—it's for you——

MRS. WADHURST (*astonished*) : For me? How very curious——

PIGGIE: Give me a cocktail, Bogey—I haven't had one at
all yet and I'm exhausted——

MRS. WADHURST (*at telephone*) : Hallo—what—who?—
I'm afraid I don't quite understand——

BOGEY (*giving* PIGGIE *a cocktail*) : Here you are—it's a
bit weak——

MRS. WADHURST (*still floundering*) : —I think there
must be some mistake—just a moment—— (*To* PIGGIE.) It's
for you, Lady Maureen—a Mrs. Rawlingson——

PIGGIE (*laughing*) : Now isn't that the most extraordinary coincidence—— (*She takes the telephone.*) —Hallo—
yes—speaking—— (*She listens and her face changes.*) —Oh
yes, of course, how stupid of me—— (*She looks hurriedly at
the* WADHURSTS, *then at* PETER.) I'm so awfully sorry, I only

just came in—— Oh, what a shame—no, no, no, it doesn't matter a bit—— No—indeed you must call me up the first moment he gets over it—— Yes—I expect it was—yes—— Good-bye.

> She slowly hangs up the receiver, looking at the WADHURSTS in complete bewilderment. She makes a sign to PETER over MRS. WADHURST's shoulder, but he only shakes his head.

PIGGIE (*brightly, but with intense meaning*) : That was Mrs. Rawlingson.

PETER: Good God!

PIGGIE (*with purpose, sitting next to* MRS. WADHURST) : Did you ever meet the Rawlingsons out East?

MRS. WADHURST: No—I don't know them.

PIGGIE: Maud and I stayed with them too, you know.

MRS. WADHURST: Where?

PIGGIE: It was in Malaya somewhere, I think—I do get so muddled.

MRS. WADHURST: I think we should have heard of them if they lived in Malaya.

> PETER *meanwhile has gone to the piano and started to strum idly—he begins to hum lightly at the same time.*

PETER (*humming to a waltz refrain, slightly indistinctly, but clearly enough for* PIGGIE *to hear*) : If these are not them who are they? Who are they? Who are they?

> PIGGIE *rises and saunters over to the piano.*

PIGGIE: Play the other bit, dear, out of the second act—— (*She hums*)—you know—"I haven't the faintest idea—— Oh no—I haven't the faintest idea."

PETER (*changing tempo*) : "Under the light of the moon, dear—you'd better find out pretty soon, dear."

CLARE: What on earth's that out of?

PIGGIE: Don't be *silly,* Clare—all I ask is that you shouldn't be *silly!*

CLARE (*understanding*) : Oh yes—I see.

There is silence except for PETER'S *playing—everyone looks covertly at the* WADHURSTS. PIGGIE *goes over to* MR. WADHURST.

PIGGIE (*with determination*) : What ship did you come home in?

MR. WADHURST: The *Naldera.*

ALLY: P & O?

MRS. WADHURST: Yes.

PIGGIE: I suppose you got on at Singapore?

MR. WADHURST: No, Penang.

PIGGIE (*the light breaking*) : Penang! Of course, Penang.

MRS. WADHURST: Yes, we have some friends there, so we went by train from Singapore and stayed with them for a couple of days before catching the boat.

PIGGIE (*sunk again*) : Oh yes—yes, I see.

PETER (*at piano, humming to march time*) : "When you hear those drums rat-a-plan—rat-a-plan—find out the name of the place if you can—la la la la la la la la——"

PIGGIE (*persevering*) : How far is your house from the sea? Maud and I were arguing about it for hours the other day——

MR. WADHURST: It's right on the sea.

PIGGIE: That's exactly what I said, but you know Maud's so vague—she never remembers a thing——

CLARE: I suppose it's hell hot all the year round where you are?

MRS. WADHURST: Yes, the climate is a little trying, but one gets used to it.

BOGEY: Are you far from Kuala Lumpur.

MRS. WADHURST: Yes, a long way.

BOGEY: Oh, I knew some people in Kuala Lumpur once.

MR. WADHURST: What were their names?

BOGEY: Damn it, I've forgotten—something like Harrison——

PIGGIE (*helpfully*) : Morrison?

ALLY: Williamson?

PETER: Lightfoot?

BOGEY: No, it's gone——

PIGGIE (*irritably*) : Never mind—it couldn't matter less really, could it?

MRS. WADHURST (*rising*) : I'm afraid we must really go now, Lady Maureen——

PIGGIE: Oh no—please——

MRS. WADHURST: We have to dress because we're dining and going to the theatre—that's the one thing we do miss dreadfully in Pendarla—the theatre——

CLARE: We miss it a good deal here, too.

PIGGIE (*remembering everything*) : Pendarla—oh dear, what a long way away it seems—dear Mrs. Wadhurst— (*She shoots a triumphant glance at* PETER.) —it's been so lovely having this little peep at you—you and Mr. Wadhurst must come and dine quietly one night and we'll go to another theatre——

MRS. WADHURST: That would be delightful—Fred——

MR. WADHURST: Good-bye.

PIGGIE: Peter—come and say good-bye to Mr. and Mrs. Wadhurst.

PETER (*coming over and shaking hands*): Good-bye—I can never tell you how grateful I am to you for having been so kind and hospitable to my wife——

MRS. WADHURST: Next time, I hope you'll come and call on us too.

PETER: I should love to.

MRS. WADHURST: Good-bye.

CLARE: Good-bye——

Everybody says good-bye and shakes hands, PETER *opens the door for the* WADHURSTS *and they go out on a wave of popularity. He goes out into the hall with them closing the door after him.* PIGGIE *collapses on to the sofa.*

PIGGIE (*hysterically*): Oh, my God, that was the most awful half an hour I've ever spent——

CLARE: I thought it all went down like a dinner.

PIGGIE: I remember it all now, we stayed one night with them on our way from Siam—a man in Bangkok had wired to them or something——

ALLY: That was a nice bit you did about the old native dancing with a sword——

PIGGIE: Oh dear, they must have thought I was drunk.

PETER *re-enters.*

PETER: Next time you travel, my darling, I suggest you keep a diary.

PIGGIE: Wasn't it frightful—poor angels—I must ring up Maud—— (*She dials a number.*) I think they had a heavenly time though, don't you—I mean they couldn't have noticed a thing——

PETER: Oh no, the whole affair was managed with the utmost subtlety—I congratulate you——

PIGGIE: Don't be sour—Peter—— (*At telephone.*) Hallo—Maud?—darling, it's not the Rawlingsons at all, it's the Wadhursts—— (*To everybody.*) Good heavens, I never gave them Maud's address. (*At telephone.*) I forgot to give them your address—how can you be so unkind, Maud, you ought to be ashamed of yourself—they're absolute pets, both of them——

PETER: Come on, Ally, I've got to dress——

ALLY: All right——

CLARE: Shall I see you on Sunday?

ALLY: Yes—I'll be over——

PIGGIE (*at telephone*): —they had a lovely time and everybody was divine to them——

CLARE: Come on, Bogey, we must go, too——

PIGGIE: Wait a minute, don't leave me—I've got to do my feet—— (*At telephone*) —no, I was talking to Clare—— My dear, I know, she rang me up too—she's staying with Norman—Phyllis will be as sour as a quince——

PETER *and* ALLY *go off talking.*

CLARE: Darling, I really *must* go——

PIGGIE (*at telephone*): —all right—I'll try to get hold of them in the morning and put them off—I do think it's horrid of you though, after all, they were frightfully sweet to us— I've done all I can—well, there's no need to get into a rage, I'm the one to get into a rage—yes, you are, I can hear you— your teeth are chattering like dice in a box—— Oh, all right! (*She hangs up.*) Maud's impossible——

CLARE: Listen, Piggie——

PIGGIE: Wait just one minute, I've got to get the things to do my feet——

She rushes out of the room.

CLARE: I really don't see why we should all wait about—— (*She suddenly sees* MR. BURNHAM.) Oh—hallo.

MR. BURNHAM (*nervously*) : Hallo.

CLARE: I thought you'd left with your mother and father.

MR. BURNHAM: They weren't my mother and father—I'm from Freeman's. I've brought the designs for the Commander's speed boat—Mr. Driscoll couldn't come——

CLARE: Well, you'd better wait—he'll be back soon——

MR. BURNHAM: I'm afraid I can't wait much longer—I have to get back to the shop——

CLARE: You should have piped up before——

BOGEY: Listen, Clare, we must push off——

CLARE: All right.

MR. BURNHAM *retires again into the shadows as* PIGGIE *returns with several bottles, a towel and a pair of scissors. She sits on the sofa and takes her shoes and stockings off.*

PIGGIE: —The trouble with Maud is, she's too insular——

CLARE: Are you driving down on Saturday?

PIGGIE: Yes—I promised to stop off at Godalming and have a cutlet with Freda on the way—do you want to come?

CLARE: You know perfectly well I hate Freda's guts.

PIGGIE (*beginning on her feet*) : All right, darling—I'll expect you in the afternoon——

The telephone rings—PIGGIE *reaches for it with one hand and goes on painting her toe nails with the other— at telephone:*

Hallo—yes. Oh, David, I'm *so* sorry—I completely forgot——

> CLARE *and* BOGEY *hiss good-bye at her, she waves to*
> *them, and they go out.*

I couldn't help it, I had to be sweet to some people that
Maud and I stayed with in Malaya—— Oh! David darling,
don't be so soured-up—yes, of course I do, don't be so
silly—— No, I'm quite alone doing my feet—well, I can't
help that, I happen to *like* them red—well, after all they are
my feet, I suppose I can paint them blue if I want to——

> MR. BURNHAM *begins to tiptoe out of the room, he*
> *leaves his roll of designs on the table.* PIGGIE *catches sight*
> *of him just as he is gingerly opening the door.*

(*To* MR. BURNHAM.) Oh, good-bye—it's been absolutely
lovely, you're the sweetest family I've ever met in my
life——

CURTAIN

NOEL COWARD, in the 1920's and 1930's, was a household word—in the best households, at least. He stood for wit, charm, the latest ties from Paris, the latest theatrical gossip from New York. The public thought of him as a playboy; he let them think it, because he loved to shock. But he worked extremely hard at his craft, writing, producing, directing, starring in (or any combination thereof) over fifty plays, composing lyrics and music for over a hundred songs.

Mr. Coward was born in England in 1899. He made his first stage appearance at twelve, in a children's play called *The Goldfish*. He played a mussel. As a child actor he got the toughest training there is: playing with a traveling repertory company. One of his fellow child-actors was Gertrude Lawrence, who became his lifelong friend and frequent co-star.

At eighteen, Mr. Coward wrote a play and began dreaming of New York: ". . . Broadway by night. . . . Its splendors and its noise and its crowds haunted my imagination. Its gigantic sky signs dazzled my dreams, flashing in a myriad of lights, with unfailing regularity, the two words, 'Noel Coward.'" In 1925 a few lights, if not a "myriad," flashed an advertisement for his first play, *The Vortex*. He was famous.

After many successes in London and New York, he wrote a romantic comedy called *Private Lives*. He sent it to his friend

Gertrude Lawrence, with the idea that they might play in it together. Miss Lawrence promptly cabled Mr. Coward her reaction: NOTHING WRONG THAT CAN'T BE FIXED. He replied: THE ONLY THING THAT MIGHT REQUIRE FIXING IS YOUR PERFORMANCE.

Mr. Coward's other plays include *Blithe Spirit*, which was famous for Margaret Rutherford's portrayal of a zany fortune-teller who makes her first-act entrance on a bicycle. "Hands Across the Sea" is one of a series of nine one-act plays called *Tonight at 8:30*. In the original production, Noel Coward played Commander Peter Gilpin, and Gertrude Lawrence played his wife.

A handy introduction to his work is *Three Plays*, which includes in one volume *Hay Fever, Blithe Spirit,* and *Private Lives.* There are several available recordings of his songs sung by himself. A record called *Noel and Gertie* includes, on one side, Mr. Coward and Miss Lawrence in scenes from *Private Lives* and other Coward plays; and on the other side, Mr. Coward singing, of course.

MEL BROOKS and
CARL REINER

The 2,000-Year-Old Man

"The 2,000-Year-Old Man" was created by Mel Brooks and Carl Reiner as a recorded interview, not a printed one. Mr. Brooks played the 2,000-Year-Old Man; Mr. Reiner played the announcer.

ANNOUNCER: About four days ago a plane landed in Idlewild Airport. The plane came from the Middle East bearing a man who claims to be 2,000 years old. He spent the last six days at the Mayo Clinic. Sir, is it true that you are 2,000 years old?

2,000-YEAR-OLD-MAN: Yes, I'll be . . . I'm not yet, I'll be 2,000 October 16th.

ANNOUNCER: You'll be 2,000? When were you born?

2,000-YEAR-OLD MAN: When I was born, oh,—October 16th, I'll be 2,000 years young, how we say, young, you know, not to curse ourselves. We was little groups of us, sitting in caves, looking in the sun and scared, you know. We didn't know—we were very dumb and stupid. You want to know something, *we were so dumb that we didn't even know who was a lady.*

ANNOUNCER: But they were—

2,000-YEAR-OLD MAN: They was with us . . . we didn't know who they were. We didn't know who was the ladies and who was fellas.

ANNOUNCER: How did you find out that they were ladies?

2,000-YEAR-OLD MAN: A cute fat guy, you could have mistaken him for a lady, you know, soft and cute.

ANNOUNCER: Who was the person who discovered the female?

2,000-YEAR-OLD MAN: Bernie.

ANNOUNCER: Who was Bernie?

2,000-YEAR-OLD MAN: Bernie, one of the first leaders of our group.

ANNOUNCER: And he discovered the female?

2,000-YEAR-OLD MAN: Yes.

ANNOUNCER: How did it happen? How did it come to pass?

2,000-YEAR-OLD MAN: He said, "Hey! There's ladies here."

ANNOUNCER: I'm very interested to find out how Bernie discovered the woman.

2,000-YEAR-OLD MAN: One morning, he got up smiling. He said I think there's ladies here. So I said, "what do you mean?"—you know? So he said, "cause in the night I was *thrilled and delighted*"—see?—so then he went into such a story that, it's thousands of years later, I still blush . . . terrible.

ANNOUNCER: Sir, could you give us the secret of your longevity?

2,000-YEAR-OLD MAN: Well, the major thing, the major thing, is that I *never, ever* touch fried food. I don't eat it, I wouldn't look at it and I don't touch it. And never run for a bus; there'll always be another. Even if you're late from work. Never run for a bus. I never ran, I just strolled, jaunty, jolly, walking to the bus stop.

ANNOUNCER: Yes, well, there were no buses in the time of Herod.

2,000-YEAR-OLD MAN: No, in my time. . . .

ANNOUNCER: What were the means of transportation then?

2,000-YEAR-OLD MAN: Mostly fear.

ANNOUNCER: Fear transported you?

2,000-YEAR-OLD MAN: Fear, yes. An animal would growl, you would go two miles in a minute.

ANNOUNCER: But I suppose you had—

2,000-YEAR-OLD MAN: Fear would be the main propulsion.

ANNOUNCER: Yes, but I think most people are interested in living a long and fruitful life, as you have. You mentioned—

2,000-YEAR-OLD MAN: Fruit is good, too. You mentioned fruit. Fruit kept me going for 140 years once when I was on a very strict diet. Mainly nectarines. I love that fruit— half a peach, half a plum, a hell of a fruit. I love it.

ANNOUNCER: Sir—

2,000-YEAR-OLD MAN: Not too cold, not too hot, you know, just nice.

ANNOUNCER: What is—?

2,000-YEAR-OLD MAN: Even a rotten one is good, that's how much I love them. I'd rather eat a rotten nectarine than a fine plum; what do you think of that?

ANNOUNCER: I can understand that.

2,000-YEAR-OLD MAN: Yes, that's how much I love them.

ANNOUNCER: Yes, I can understand that.

2,000-YEAR-OLD MAN: Yes, yes, some good things.

ANNOUNCER: Sir, what did you do for a living?

2,000-YEAR-OLD MAN: Well, many years ago, thousands of years ago, there was no heavy industry.

ANNOUNCER: We know that.

2,000-YEAR-OLD MAN: The most things that we manufactured, the most things we ever made, was we would take a piece of wood, and rub it and rub it and clean it and look at it and hit earth with it, and hit a tree with it.

ANNOUNCER: For what purpose?

2,000-YEAR-OLD MAN: Just to keep busy! There was nothing else to do. There was absolutely nothing to do. We had no jobs, don't you see?

ANNOUNCER: What other jobs were there? There must have been something else besides hitting a tree—

2,000-YEAR-OLD MAN: No—

ANNOUNCER:—with a piece of stick.

2,000-YEAR-OLD MAN: Well, hitting a tree with a piece of stick was already a good job, you couldn't get that job, you know.

ANNOUNCER: What jobs—?

2,000-YEAR-OLD MAN: Mainly there was sitting and looking in the sky was a big job and another job was watching each other. That was light work, looking at each other.

ANNOUNCER: What language did you speak at that time?

2,000-YEAR-OLD MAN: We spoke rock, basic rock.

ANNOUNCER: Basic rock. That was before Hebrew?

2,000-YEAR-OLD MAN: Yes, 200 years before Hebrew was the rock language or rock talk.

ANNOUNCER: Could you give us an example of that?

2,000-YEAR-OLD MAN: Yes. (*thinking*) Hey, put that rock down. Don't throw that rock at me. Hey, what are you doing with that rock there?

ANNOUNCER: I see—

2,000-YEAR-OLD MAN: Put that rock away.

ANNOUNCER: I see.

2,000-YEAR-OLD MAN: That was the rock talk.

ANNOUNCER: Now, do you remember your Hebrew?

2,000-YEAR-OLD MAN: Yes, I—

ANNOUNCER: Would you speak to us—?

2,000-YEAR-OLD MAN: I think I remember it fluently.

ANNOUNCER: Because I understand modern Hebrew is different from the archaic—

2,000-YEAR-OLD MAN: Yes, it's different in some of the phonetic alliterations and pattrens.

ANNOUNCER: Could we hear an example of the ancient Hebrew?

2,000-YEAR-OLD MAN: The very ancient Hebrew is . . . "Oh, hi there, hello. Hello there, how are you? I'm . . . all right . . . how are . . . you?"

ANNOUNCER: That's English.

2,000-YEAR-OLD MAN: Oh, wait. Wait . . . .

ANNOUNCER: Do you remember any Hebrew?

2,000-YEAR-OLD MAN: Very little, I think. I don't think I remember it. I must have forgot a great deal of it.

ANNOUNCER: I think you forgot it all, sir.

2,000-YEAR-OLD MAN: Maybe all, maybe all.

ANNOUNCER: Yes.

2,000-YEAR-OLD MAN: It's thousands of years since I needed it.

ANNOUNCER: Now, sir, did you ever have any formal job as we know it today?

2,000-YEAR-OLD MAN: Well, I was a manufacturer, I was an owner.

ANNOUNCER: What kind of a factory did you have?

2,000-YEAR-OLD MAN: I used to make the Star of David, the Jewish Star.

ANNOUNCER: Oh, yes, the little thing you wear—

2,000-YEAR-OLD MAN: Yes, as soon as religion came in, I was one of the first in that.

ANNOUNCER: And how—?

2,000-YEAR-OLD MAN: I figured, this is a good thing—

ANNOUNCER: And how did you make them? Did you have tools?

2,000-YEAR-OLD MAN: Well, we didn't have lathes. I employed six men, see, each with a point and they used to run together at great speeds, thereby fusing the thing and making a. . . .

ANNOUNCER: Thus making a star?

2,000-YEAR-OLD MAN: Yes, we would make two a day because of the many accidents.

ANNOUNCER: What—?

2,000-YEAR-OLD MAN: You have six men running at high speeds with points. . . .

ANNOUNCER: I see—

2,000-YEAR-OLD MAN: Plenty accidents.

ANNOUNCER: I see. You never thought of going into anything else?

2,000-YEAR-OLD MAN: No . . . I had an offer once.

ANNOUNCER: What was that?

2,000-YEAR-OLD MAN: A fella came to me—Simon. Or was it

Peter? No, it was Simon. Let it be Peter. Make that Simon.

ANNOUNCER: What did Simon ask you to do?

2,000-YEAR-OLD MAN: Well, he said, "We have a new thing, a new item, a winner, looks like a winning item, it's gonna be a big seller . . . it's called a cross." I looked at it and I turned it over and I looked on all sides of it, and I said, "It's simple, it's too simple." I didn't know then it was eloquent.

ANNOUNCER: You mean—?

2,000-YEAR-OLD MAN: I didn't know it would be such a hit.

ANNOUNCER: You turned him down?

2,000-YEAR-OLD MAN: I said, "I'm sorry, but I'm too busy." See, I could have fired four men. Two men run together—bang—you got a cross. I would have had over $100 today if I went in crosses.

ANNOUNCER: It's a shame—

2,000-YEAR-OLD MAN: Because they're in everywhere today . . . just look up. Find a pointy building and look up.

ANNOUNCER: By the way, sir, are you married?

2,000-YEAR-OLD MAN: I have been married several hundred times.

ANNOUNCER: Several hundred times?

2,000-YEAR-OLD MAN: Yes, yes.

ANNOUNCER: Do you remember all your wives?

2,000-YEAR-OLD MAN: One I remember very well.

ANNOUNCER: Which one was that?

2,000-YEAR-OLD MAN: The third one, Shirley, I remember her—a redhead.

ANNOUNCER: I'm afraid to ask the next question. You had many hundreds of wives—

2,000-YEAR-OLD MAN: Hundreds, hundreds wives—

ANNOUNCER: How many children do you have?

2,000-YEAR-OLD MAN: (*slowly*) I have over 42,000 children —and not one comes to visit me. . . .

ANNOUNCER: Oh, that's terrible, sir.

2,000-YEAR-OLD MAN: You bet. How they forget a father, sure, children, that's how they are.

ANNOUNCER: That's awful, sir, that's really awful. You mean to say there isn't one daughter that favors you—?

2,000-YEAR-OLD MAN: Many daughters—but, you know how they are, children—good luck to them—let them go and be happy—I don't want—listen—let them be happy—as long as they're happy, I don't care. But they could send a note and write, "how are you, Pop, how you doing, Pop?" I don't get a Pop out of them.

ANNOUNCER: Sir, you must have known some great men in your time. You did travel throughout the world.

2,000-YEAR-OLD MAN: I knew the great and the near great.

ANNOUNCER: Could I ask you about these?

2,000-YEAR-OLD MAN: Certainly, I'll tell you the true, whether I knew or not.

ANNOUNCER: For instance, people are very interested in somebody like Joan of Arc. A lot has been written about her, and we read about her—

2,000-YEAR-OLD MAN: Ah, what a cutie!

ANNOUNCER: You *knew* Joan of Arc?

2,000-YEAR-OLD MAN: I *went* with her, dummy, I *went* with her.

ANNOUNCER: Nowhere in history do we know of Joan going with anybody.

2,000-YEAR-OLD MAN: Well, they don't print that. They don't print everything.

ANNOUNCER: You didn't marry her?

2,000-YEAR-OLD MAN: No, no, I didn't marry her because she was on a mission, you know. She used to say to me, she used to say to me, "I've got to save France." I used to say, "Look, I've got to wash up. You save France and after you'll save France, I'll wash up." Her in her way, me in mine, you know?

ANNOUNCER: How did you feel about her being burned at the stake?

2,000-YEAR-OLD MAN: Terrible.

ANNOUNCER: Sir, how about some of the legendary characters who supposedly might have existed? For instance, Robin Hood? Did he exist?

2,000-YEAR-OLD MAN: Oh, yes, lovely man—ran around in the forest.

ANNOUNCER: Did he really steal from the rich and give to the poor?

2,000-YEAR-OLD MAN: No, he didn't—

ANNOUNCER: He didn't?

2,000-YEAR-OLD MAN: He stole from everybody and kept everything.

ANNOUNCER: Well, how did legend—?

2,000-YEAR-OLD MAN: How did legend—?

ANNOUNCER: How did legend spring up that he was such a—?

2,000-YEAR-OLD MAN: He had a fella, Marty, Marty the press agent. He took ads in old scrolls, "He took from the rich and gave to the poor."

ANNOUNCER: I see—

2,000-YEAR-OLD MAN: Who knew? He'd give you such a knock in the head when he robbed you, you wouldn't remember anything anyway.

ANNOUNCER: So in other words, we—

2,000-YEAR-OLD MAN: He was a tough guy.

ANNOUNCER: I hate to have our legendary figures smashed like this.

2,000-YEAR-OLD MAN: Well, I hate to smash them for you.

ANNOUNCER: You've lived for so long. Did you ever have an accident?

2,000-YEAR-OLD MAN: An accent, always.

ANNOUNCER: An *accident*.

2,000-YEAR-OLD MAN: Yes. Yes, in the year '61 I was hit—I was run over by seven men fleeing a lion. They ran me over.

ANNOUNCER: And that's the extent of all the—?

2,000-YEAR-OLD MAN: But they didn't have insurance, I didn't have insurance. There was no such thing then.

ANNOUNCER: No.

2,000-YEAR-OLD MAN: You laid there till you got better.

ANNOUNCER: In the 2,000 years you've lived, you've seen a lot of changes.

2,000-YEAR-OLD MAN: Yes, I certainly have—

ANNOUNCER: What is the biggest change you've seen?

2,000-YEAR-OLD MAN: In 2,000 years, the greatest thing mankind ever devised, I think, in mine umble opinion, is Saran wrap! You can put a sandwich in it, you can look through it, you can touch it and put it over your face and fool around and everything.

ANNOUNCER: You equate this with—?

2,000-YEAR-OLD MAN: I love it. You can put three olives in it and make a little one. You can put ten sandwiches in and make a big Saran. Whatever you want, it's clean and it sticks.

ANNOUNCER: You equate this with the—?

2,000-YEAR-OLD MAN: You can look right through it.

ANNOUNCER: You equate this with man's discovery of space?

2,000-YEAR-OLD MAN: That was good . . . that was good. That was a good thing.

ANNOUNCER: Well, sir—

2,000-YEAR-OLD MAN: Space, finding space. That was good.

ANNOUNCER: We don't have too much more time but we all here would like to know your code.

2,000-YEAR-OLD MAN: Well, all right, is this it?

ANNOUNCER: You're on.

2,000-YEAR-OLD MAN: My farewell?

ANNOUNCER: Your farewell address.

2,000-YEAR-OLD MAN: Hello there, this is 2,000 years talking to you from the depths of back there when we was and now I'm still and they not. And I just want to say, keep a smile on your face and stay out of a Ferrari or any small Italian car. Stay out of them and I want to tell you that it's been a wonderful 2,000 years and you've been a wonderful civilization, and it's been a thrill living for 2,000 years, and, eat a nectarine, it's the *best* fruit ever made!

MEL BROOKS and CARL REINER invented the 2,000-Year-Old Man one night at a party, and recorded some interviews with him shortly thereafter. They worked out the skit in the way Nichols and May operated, feeding each other lines and improvising as they went along. The record, made in 1960, was Mel Brooks's first work as a performer. Before that, he had been a comedy writer, notably for Sid Caesar's *Your Show of Shows.* In 1965 he and Buck Henry created the television series *Get Smart.* After that, people began to ask Mr. Brooks what he was going to do next. He developed a convenient answer—that he was writing a musical comedy based on the life of Hitler. At some point he must have realized that he had an interesting idea there, because he ended up writing and directing a movie called *The Producers,* which concerns the world's worst musical comedy, *Springtime for Hitler.* Mr. Brooks won an Oscar for this screenplay. Mr. Brooks was born in 1927, and may he live for 2,000 more years. He is married to the actress Anne Bancroft.

Carl Reiner, born in 1922, acted in summer stock and on Broadway. In 1950 he joined *Your Show of Shows.* "It was the happiest thing that ever happened to me," he says. He emceed the program and acted in the skits with Sid Caesar and Imogene Coca. He won Emmy awards for his acting on two later television shows that starred Sid Caesar. Mr. Reiner often contributed jokes and ideas to the Caesar shows, and in 1961 he originated and produced *The Dick Van Dyke Show.* He has also written a novel, *Enter Laughing,* which was made into a play and a movie.

THOMAS MEEHAN

Yma Dream

In this dream, which I have had on the night of the full moon for the past three months, I am giving a cocktail party in honor of Yma Sumac, the Peruvian singer. This is strange at once, for while I have unbounded admiration for four-octave voices, I have never met Miss Sumac, and, even in a dream, it seems unlikely that I should be giving her a party. No matter. She and I are in the small living room of my apartment, on Charles Street, in Greenwich Village, and we are getting along famously. I have told her several of my Swedish-dialect stories, and she has reciprocated by singing for me, in Quechua, a medley of Andean folk songs. Other guests are expected momentarily. I have no idea, however, who any of them will be. Miss Sumac is wearing a blue ball gown and I am in white tie and tails. Obviously, despite the somewhat unfashionable neighborhood and the cramped quarters of my apartment, it is to be a pretty swell affair. In any case, I have spread several dishes of Fritos about the room, and on what is normally my typing table there is a bowl of hot *glügg*.

The doorbell rings. A guest! I go to the door, and there, to my astonished delight, is Ava Gardner. This is going to be a bit of all right, I think.

"Tom, darling!" she says, embracing me warmly. "How wonderful of you to have asked me."

In my waking hours, unfortunately, I have never met Miss Gardner. In my dream, though, my guests seem to know me rather intimately, while, oddly, none of them seem to know each other. Apparently it is their strong common affection for me that has brought them to Charles Street. For my part, although I immediately recognize each guest as he or she arrives, I have no memory of having ever met any of them, or, for that matter, of having invited them to a party in my apartment. On with the dream, however. "Miss Ava Gardner," I say, "I'd like you to meet Miss Yma Sumac."

"Charmed," says Miss Sumac.

"Delighted," counters Miss Gardner.

"Ah, but Tom," says Miss Sumac, with an enchanting laugh (which runs up the scale from E above middle C to C above high C), "let us not, on this of all occasions, be formal. *Por favor,* introduce each guest only by the first name, so that we may all quickly become—how shall I say?—*amigos.*"

Typical Peruvian friendliness, I think, and reintroduce the two. "Ava, Yma," I say.

We sit around for some time, sipping *glügg* and munching Fritos. Things seem to be going well. The doorbell rings again. The second guest is a man—Abba Eban, the former Israeli Ambassador to the United Nations. Again I make the introductions, and bowing to the wishes of the guest of honor, keep things on a first-name basis. "Abba, Yma; Abba, Ava," I say.

I stifle a grin, but neither Miss Sumac nor my two other guests see anything amusing in the exchange. We chat. The bell rings again, and I am pleased to find Oona O'Neill, Charlie Chaplin's wife, at the door. She is alone. I bring her into the room. "Oona, Yma; Oona, Ava; Oona, Abba," I say.

We are standing in a circle now, smiling brightly but not talking much. I sense a slight strain, but the party is young and may yet come to life. The bell again. It is another man—Ugo Betti, the Italian playwright. A bit hurriedly, I introduce him to the circle. "Ugo, Yma; Ugo, Ava; Ugo, Oona; Ugo, Abba," I say.

Miss Sumac gives me an enigmatic glance that I try to interpret. Boredom? Thirst? No, she looks almost *irritated*. Hastily, I replenish everyone's glass. For some reason, I begin to hope that no other guests have been invited. The doorbell rings once again, however, and I open the door on two lovely actresses, Ona Munson and Ida Lupino. This gives me a happy inspiration for my introductions. "Ona and Ida," I say, "surely you know Yma and Ava? Ida, Ona—Oona, Abba." Damn! It doesn't come out even. "Ida, Ona—Ugo," I finish lamely.

I have scarcely given Miss Munson and Miss Lupino their first drinks when I am again summoned to the door. My guests stand stony-faced as I usher in the new arrival, the young Aga Khan. He is looking exceptionally well turned out in a dinner jacket with a plaid cummerbund. Smiling too cheerfully, I introduce him to the waiting group. "Folks," I say, using a word I have always detested, "here's the Aga Khan! *You* know." But there is silence, so I must continue. "Aga—Yma, Ava, Oona, Ona 'n' Ida, Abba 'n' Ugo."

The Aga Khan and Mr. Eban, I notice, take an immediate dislike to each other, and I begin to feel an unmistakable pall descending over my party. I suggest a game of charades. This is met with glacial looks from everyone, including Miss Gardner, whose earlier affection for me has now totally vanished. When the doorbell rings this time, everybody turns and glares at the door. I open it and discover another pair— Ira Wolfert, the novelist, and Ilya Ehrenburg, the *Russian* novelist. The latter, I know, is quite a man-of-the-world, so I try a new approach. "Ilya," I say, "why don't you just introduce yourself and Ira? You know all these lovely people, don't you?"

"*Nyet,*" says Mr. Ehrenburg. "Can't say that I do."

"Oh, all *right,*" I say. "Ilya, Ira, here's Yma, Ava, Oona. Ilya, Ira—Ona, Ida, Abba, Ugo, Aga."

I ask Miss Sumac to sing for us. She refuses. We continue with the *glügg* and some hopelessly inane small talk. Mr. Eban and the Aga Khan stand at opposite sides of the room, eying each other. I begin to wish I'd never given the goddam party. Ona Munson jostles Ugo Betti's elbow by accident, spilling his drink. I spring forward to put them at their ease, whipping a handkerchief from my pocket. "Never mind!" I cry. "No damage done! Ugo, you go get yourself another drink. I'll just wipe this *glügg* off the, uh, *rügg.*" The guests fix me with narrowed eyes. At this moment, Eva Gabor, the

Hungarian actress, sweeps through the door, which I have cleverly left open. Unaware of the way things are going, she embraces me and turns, beaming, to meet the others. Inevitably, I must make the introductions. I start rapidly. "Eva, meet Yma and Ava and Oona—" But then I find that Miss Gabor is pausing to hug each guest in turn, so I am forced to make the remaining introductions separately. "Eva, Ona; Eva, Ida; Eva, Ugo; Eva, Abba; Eva, Ilya; Eva, Ira; Eva, Aga."

This is a *terrible* party. All the men have bunched up. We stand in a circle, glowering at one another. I can think of nothing to say. I feel oddly hemmed in, like a man who is about to be stoned to death.

"Am I late?" asks the actress Uta Hagen gaily as she comes tripping into the room.

"No, no!" I say, gallantly taking her arm and steering her at once toward the punch bowl and away from the others.

"Please have the common decency to introduce your guests to one another," says Miss Sumac, in a cold monotone. "And in the proper manner."

In the dream, Yma Sumac seems to have some kind of hold over me, and I must do as she wishes. "O.K., O.K.," I snap crossly. "Uta, Yma; Uta, Ava; Uta, Oona; Uta, Ona; Uta, Ida; Uta, Ugo; Uta, Abba; Uta, Ilya, Uta, Ira; Uta, Aga; Uta, Eva." I turn to see if this has placated Miss Sumac, but she coldly ignores me. I have begun to hate her. Then I discover that the *glügg* has run out, and I am forced to offer my guests rye-and-7-Up. In the hope that no further company will arrive, I silently close the door. The bell rings instantly, however, and I feel a chill run down my spine. I pretend not to hear it.

"Answer the door," Miss Sumac says peremptorily. My circle of guests moves menacingly toward me. With a plummeting heart, I open the door. Standing before me, in immaculate evening dress, is a sturdy, distinguished-looking man. He is the Polish concert pianist Mieczyslaw Horszowski.

"Come in, Mieczyslaw!" I cry, with tears in my eyes. "I've never been so glad to see anyone in my whole life!"

And here, always, my dream ends.

THOMAS MEEHAN is a shadowy figure who may be glimpsed now and then at New York City's cultural centers: the movie houses on Forty-second Street, the Metropolitan Opera (where he often translates the operas for his fellow opera-goers: *"Lucia di Lammermoor*—Lucy from Lammermoor.") He is frequently found crouching in front of his television set watching the Late Show. He writes about these and other matters, usually in *The New Yorker,* where his work has been published since the 1950's. He is one of two or three excellent young contenders for the crown presently worn by S. J. Perelman.

Curiously flirtatious about his age, Mr. Meehan says only that he was born "in the early years of the Depression." He grew up in Suffern, New York, and graduated from Hamilton College in Clinton, New York. Next, he says, "dragged screaming into the United States Army," he served during the Korean War in the Counter Intelligence Corps in Stuttgart, Germany, "well out of range of Red Chinese mortars." In 1956 he joined *The New Yorker's* editorial staff. He has also contributed to *Esquire,* the *Saturday Evening Post,* and other magazines.

Until recently, Mr. Meehan and his wife ("an accomplished editor, short-order cook, and tap dancer") divided their time between an apartment in Greenwich Village and a farmhouse in Connecticut. However, as this book goes to press and "as war clouds gather over Cambodia and the Dow-Jones average has no place to go but down," they are living in a village on the French Riviera.

A collection of Thomas Meehan's stories was published in 1967 under the title *Yma, Ava, Yma, Abba, Yma, Oona, Yma, Ida, Yma, Aga . . . and Others.*

FRANK SULLIVAN

The Cliché Expert Testifies on War

Q: Mr. Arbuthnot, if you are prepared, I should like today to go into the subject of the cliché as applied to war.

A: I am at your service, Mr. Smith.

Q: Thank you. Mr. Arbuthnot, what is war?

A: That depends on how you look at it.

Q: What do you mean by that?

A: It depends on whether you agree with Hitler or with General Sherman. Sherman thought that war was hell. Hitler thinks war is an ennobling experience in whose purifying fires the souls of men are cleansed and sanctified.

Q: What does war do?

A: War impends.

Q: You mean that Europe's fate—

A: Is hanging in the balance. I mean also that Europe is

sitting on the top of a smoldering volcano. The international situation is grave.

Q: How do you know that the international situation is grave?

A: I have it on diplomatic authority—*high* diplomatic authority. The Quai d'Orsay is making no effort to conceal its anxiety. Likewise Downing Street.

Q: Which war is it that impends, Mr. Arbuthnot?

A: The war to end war.

Q: That being the general situation, how would you describe the present state of Europe?

A: Europe is an armed camp.

Q: How would you say it is armed?

A: Europe is armed to the teeth.

Q: That is to say, the nations are eager to go to war again.

A: You mean that they are eager to appeal to the sword. But you are wrong, Mr. Smith. The nations of Europe are not eager to appeal to the sword. They want peace. Or, as a cliché expert like myself would prefer to put it, they are sincerely desirous of living in amity and concord with their neighbors.

Q: Who says so?

A: Hitler. Mussolini. The Japs.

Q: Then why are they all arming to the teeth?

A: You mean why are they arraying themselves in the full panoply of war? It is because they *have* to go to war, Mr. Smith.

Q: Why do they have to go to war?

A: Sir, to avenge their national honor.

Q: What national honor?

A: Your Honor, must I answer that question?

THE COURT: I think not, on the ground that it might tend to incriminate and degrade friendly Powers.

A: You see, Mr. Smith, Hitler does not really want war. He simply wants Germany to have a place in the sun.

Q: Can't she get a place in the sun?

A: No.

Q: Why not?

A: Because the sun is too busy never setting on the British Empire.

Q: I see. But why did Mussolini attack Ethiopia?

A: Oh, but he didn't attack Ethiopia. Ethiopia affronted the national honor of Italy.

Q: When?

A: Forty years ago, at Aduwa. And Mussolini had to avenge Italy's national honor.

Q: How?

A: By bringing the blessings of civilization to Ethiopia.

Q: I see. How about Japan, Mr. Arbuthnot?

A: Japan wants peace with a burning passion, but she must fulfill her imperial destiny.

Q: How?

A: By bringing the blessings of civilization to China. And of course, in addition to avenging their national honor, the nations must expand.

Q: Why must they expand?

A: Because they have an excess of population.

Q: Why have they got an excess of population?

A: Because they must have plenty of males to fight the wars of expansion made necessary by the excess of population. Italy must expand. Germany must expand. Japan must expand. And Britain won't contract.

Q: Which results in?

A: Which results in what is technically known as a mad scramble for power.

Q: Mr. Arbuthnot, do you care to venture a guess at the future course of events in Europe, in your capacity as a cliché expert?

A: I will do so gladly. Eventually, there will be one too many affronts to national honor. Ultimatums will be issued, and apologies demanded. Representations will be made. There will be what I like to call warlike gestures. Diplomats will hurry to the Foreign Office, where lights will be seen burning far into the night. It will be an open secret that the situation is fraught with danger. The chancelleries of Europe will express grave concern for the balance of power. Responsibility for war will be placed on the shoulders of every nation by every other nation—placed *squarely*. Every effort will be made to avert an outbreak of hostilities and avoid a worldwide conflagration.

Q: How?

A: By mobilizing the armies and rushing troops to the frontier.

Q: Then what?

A: Then Armageddon. Cry havoc. Let loose the dogs of war. Unsheath the sword. The tramp of marching feet. The glint of bayonets. The serried ranks. Zero hour. Over the top. No Man's Land. Take no prisoners. Gas. Distant booming of guns. Seventy killed in air raid. Grim-visaged war in a world gone mad with blood lust. And the song of a lark at dawn in a wheatfield running red.

Q: Who do the actual fighting?

A: The flower of a nation's youth.

Q: What is the technical name for these young men?

A: Cannon fodder, or our brave boys.

Q: What do they do?

A: They leave home and fireside, factory and plough, to do their bit.

Q: How do they do their bit?

A: By giving their all. They make the supreme sacrifice. They die a hero's death.

Q: And their reward is—

A: They are buried with full military honors and are enshrined in the hearts of their countrymen.

Q: Mr. Arbuthnot, what was it the mother didn't do?

A: She didn't raise her boy to be a soldier.

Q: And the mother who didn't raise her boy to be a soldier turned out to be which mother?

A: The Gold Star mother.

Q: Now then, after the nations have been bled white, the countries laid waste, the cities reduced to ashes and the populations to starvation, the national honors avenged, the foe repelled, and in Flanders fields the poppies blow between the crosses row on row—what happens then?

A: The dove of peace makes its appearance. There are peace overtures.

Q: Why?

A: Because there never was a good war or a bad peace.

Q: What happens then?

A: Then there is the peace conference.

Q: What does the peace conference do?

A: It liberates the oppressed and downtrodden of all nations.

Q: Then what?

A: Then the nations start arming to the teeth to avenge the next affront to their national honor by means of the next war to end war.

FRANK SULLIVAN is our nation's expert on clichés, but he writes other kinds of humor too. All of it is as much fun as a barrel of monkeys and has made him a noted specialist in tickling people pink.

Mr. Sullivan writes up a storm in Saratoga Springs, New York, "on the ancestral half-acre," where he first saw the light of day in 1892. He graduated from Cornell University in 1914, then served in the infantry during World War I. After the war he took a job on a newspaper in his home town. He had a nose for news, and he worked like a dog; so he soon reached the big time as a columnist on the New York *World,* which was staffed by many famous writers, all of them turning out funny articles to beat the band. More recently Mr. Sullivan's writing has appeared in *The New Yorker.* That magazine's readers await with bated breath his annual Yuletide poem, in which he salutes the salute-worthy personalities of the passing year. His books include *The Night the Old Nostalgia Burned Down, A Pearl in Every Oyster,* and *A Rock in Every Snowball.*

There's no time like the present for reprinting "The Cliché Expert Testifies on War." Although it was first published in 1936, it still, as they say, hits home.

JOSEPH HELLER

Milo

The following selection is part of a novel, "Catch-22," which takes place on an air force base on an island off Italy during World War II. The book's hero is Yossarian, who is in a desperate and ridiculous plight. Yossarian's problem goes roughly like this: He does not want to fly any more bombing missions. If he can convince the air force that he is crazy, he will not have to fly any more missions. But there's a catch—"Catch-22." Catch-22 of the air force regulations states that only a crazy man would want to fly bombing missions. Therefore, anyone who doesn't want to fly missions must be sane. Therefore, Yossarian must be sane and can't be discharged.

The section of "Catch-22" that follows is about one of Yossarian's friends, Milo Minderbinder.

April had been the best month of all for Milo. Lilacs bloomed in April and fruit ripened on the vine. Heartbeats quickened and old appetites were renewed. In April a livelier iris gleamed upon the burnished dove. April was spring, and in the spring Milo Minderbinder's fancy had lightly turned to thoughts of tangerines.

"Tangerines?"

"Yes, sir."

"My men would love tangerines," admitted the colonel in Sardinia who commanded four squadrons of B-26s.

"There'll be all the tangerines they can eat that you're able to pay for with money from your mess fund," Milo assured him.

"Casaba melons?"

"Are going for a song in Damascus."

"I have a weakness for casaba melons. I've always had a weakness for casaba melons."

"Just lend me one plane from each squadron, just one plane, and you'll have all the casabas you can eat that you've money to pay for."

"We buy from the syndicate?"

"And everybody has a share."

"It's amazing, positively amazing. How can you do it?"

"Mass purchasing power makes the big difference. For example, breaded veal cutlets."

"I'm not so crazy about breaded veal cutlets," grumbled the skeptical B-25 commander in the north of Corsica.

"Breaded veal cutlets are very nutritious," Milo admonished him piously. "They contain egg yolk and bread crumbs. And so are lamb chops."

"Ah, lamb chops," echoed the B-25 commander. "Good lamb chops?"

"The best," said Milo, "that the black market has to offer."

"Baby lamb chops?"

"In the cutest little pink paper panties you ever saw. Are going for a song in Portugal."

"I can't send a plane to Portugal. I haven't the authority."

"I can, once you lend the plane to me. With a pilot to fly it. And don't forget—you'll get General Dreedle."

"Will General Dreedle eat in my mess hall again?"

"Like a pig, once you start feeding him my best white fresh eggs fried in my pure creamery butter. There'll be tangerines too, and casaba melons, honeydews, filet of Dover sole, baked Alaska, and cockles and mussels."

"And everybody has a share?"

"That," said Milo, "is the most beautiful part of it."

"I don't like it," growled the uncooperative fighter-plane commander, who didn't like Milo either.

"There's an uncooperative fighter-plane commander up north who's got it in for me," Milo complained to General Dreedle. "It takes just one person to ruin the whole thing, and then you wouldn't have your fresh eggs fried in my pure creamery butter any more."

General Dreedle had the uncooperative fighter-plane commander transferred to the Solomon Islands to dig graves and replaced him with a senile colonel with bursitis and a craving for litchi nuts who introduced Milo to the B-17 general on the mainland with a yearning for Polish sausage.

"Polish sausage is going for peanuts in Cracow," Milo informed him.

"Polish sausage," sighed the general nostalgically. "You know, I'd give just about anything for a good hunk of Polish sausage. Just about anything."

"You don't have to give *anything*. Just give me one

plane for each mess hall and a pilot who will do what he's told. And a small down payment on your initial order as a token of good faith."

"But Cracow is hundreds of miles behind the enemy lines. How will you get to the sausage?"

"There's an international Polish sausage exchange in Geneva. I'll just fly the peanuts into Switzerland and exchange them for Polish sausage at the open market rate. They'll fly the peanuts back to Cracow and I'll fly the Polish sausage back to you. You buy only as much Polish sausage as you want through the syndicate. There'll be tangerines too, with only a little artificial coloring added. And eggs from Malta and Scotch from Sicily. You'll be paying the money to yourself when you buy from the syndicate, since you'll own a share, so you'll really be getting everything you buy for nothing. Doesn't that make sense?"

"Sheer genius. How in the world did you ever think of it?"

"My name is Milo Minderbinder. I am twenty-seven years old."

Milo Minderbinder's planes flew in from everywhere, the pursuit planes, bombers, and cargo ships streaming into Colonel Cathcart's field with pilots at the controls who would do what they were told. The planes were decorated with flamboyant squadron emblems illustrating such laudable ideals as Courage, Might, Justice, Truth, Liberty, Love, Honor and Patriotism that were painted out at once by Milo's mechanics with a double coat of flat white and replaced in garish purple with the stenciled name M & M ENTERPRISES, FINE FRUITS AND PRODUCE. The "M & M" in "M & M ENTERPRISES" stood for Milo & Minderbinder, and the & was inserted, Milo revealed candidly, to nullify any impression that the syndicate was a one-man operation. Planes arrived for Milo from airfields in Italy, North Africa and England, and from Air Transport Command stations in Liberia, Ascension Island, Cairo and Karachi. Pursuit planes were traded for additional cargo ships or retained for emergency invoice duty and small-parcel service; trucks and tanks were procured from the ground forces and used for short-distance road hauling. Everybody had a share, and men got fat and moved about tamely with toothpicks in their greasy lips. Milo supervised the whole expanding operation by himself. Deep otter-brown lines of preoccupation etched themselves permanently into his careworn face and gave him a harried look of sobriety and mistrust. Everybody but Yossarian thought Milo was a jerk, first for volunteering for the job of mess officer and next for taking it so seriously. Yossarian also thought that Milo was a jerk; but he also knew that Milo was a genius.

One day Milo flew away to England to pick up a load of Turkish halvah and came flying back from Madagascar leading four German bombers filled with yams, collards, mustard greens and black-eyed Georgia peas. Milo was dumfounded when he stepped down to the ground and found a contingent of armed M.P.s waiting to imprison the German pilots and confiscate their planes. *Confiscate!* The mere word was anathema to him, and he stormed back and forth in excoriating condemnation, shaking a piercing finger of rebuke in the guilt-ridden faces of Colonel Cathcart, Colonel Korn and the poor battle-scarred captain with the submachine gun who commanded the M.P.s.

"Is this Russia?" Milo assailed them incredulously at the top of his voice. *"Confiscate?"* he shrieked, as though he could not believe his own ears. "Since when is it the policy of the American government to confiscate the private property of its citizens? Shame on you! Shame on all of you for even thinking such a horrible thought."

"But Milo," Major Danby interrupted timidly, "we're at war with Germany, and those are German planes."

"They are no such thing!" Milo retorted furiously. "Those planes belong to the syndicate, and everybody has a share. *Confiscate?* How can you possibly confiscate your own private property? *Confiscate,* indeed! I've never heard anything so depraved in my whole life."

And sure enough, Milo was right, for when they looked, his mechanics had painted out the German swastikas on the wings, tails and fuselages with double coats of flat white and stenciled in the words M & M ENTERPRISES, FINE FRUITS AND PRODUCE. Right before their eyes he had transformed his syndicate into an international cartel.

Milo's argosies of plenty now filled the air. Planes poured in from Norway, Denmark, France, Germany, Austria, Italy, Yugoslavia, Romania, Bulgaria, Sweden, Finland, Poland—from everywhere in Europe, in fact, but Russia, with whom Milo refused to do business. When everybody who was going to had signed up with M & M Enterprises, Fine Fruits and Produce, Milo created a wholly owned subsidiary, M & M Enterprises, Fancy Pastry, and obtained more airplanes and more money from the mess funds for scones and crumpets from the British Isles, prune and cheese Danish from Copenhagen, éclairs, cream puffs, Napoleons and *petits fours* from Paris, Reims and Grenoble, *Kugelhopf,* pumpernickel and *Pfefferkuchen* from Berlin, *Linzer* and *Dobos Torten* from Vienna, *Strudel* from Hungary and *baklava* from Ankara. Each morning Milo sent planes aloft all over Europe and North Africa hauling long red tow signs advertising the day's specials in large square letters: "EYE ROUND, 79¢ . . . WHITING, 21¢." He boosted cash income for the syndicate by leasing tow signs to Pet Milk, Gaines Dog Food, and Noxzema. In a spirit of civic enterprise, he regularly allotted a certain amount of free aerial advertising space to General Peckem for the propagation of such messages in the public interest as NEATNESS COUNTS, HASTE MAKES WASTE, and THE FAMILY THAT PRAYS TOGETHER STAYS TOGETHER. Milo purchased spot radio announcements on Axis Sally's and Lord Haw Haw's daily propaganda broadcasts from Berlin to keep things moving. Business boomed on every battlefront.

Milo's planes were a familiar sight. They had freedom of passage everywhere, and one day Milo contracted with the American military authorities to bomb the German-held highway bridge at Orvieto and with the German military authorities to defend the highway bridge at Orvieto with antiaircraft fire against his own attack. His fee for attacking the bridge for America was the total cost of the operation plus six per cent, and his fee from Germany for defending the bridge was the same cost-plus-six agreement augmented by a merit bonus of a thousand dollars for every American plane he shot down. The consummation of these deals represented an important victory for private enterprise, he pointed out, since the armies of both countries were socialized institutions. Once the contracts were signed, there seemed to be no point in using the resources of the syndicate to bomb and defend the bridge, inasmuch as both governments had ample men and material right there to do so and were perfectly happy to contribute them, and in the end Milo realized a fantastic profit from both halves of his project for doing nothing more than signing his name twice.

The arrangements were fair to both sides. Since Milo did have freedom of passage everywhere, his planes were able to steal over in a sneak attack without alerting the German anti-aircraft gunners; and since Milo knew about the attack, he was able to alert the German antiaircraft gunners in sufficient time for them to begin firing accurately the moment the planes came into range. It was an ideal arrangement for everyone but the dead man in Yossarian's tent, who was killed over the target the day he arrived.

"I didn't kill him!" Milo kept replying passionately to Yossarian's angry protest. "I wasn't even there that day, I tell you. Do you think I was down there on the ground firing an antiaircraft gun when the planes came over?"

"But you organized the whole thing, didn't you?" Yossarian shouted back at him in the velvet darkness cloaking the path leading past the still vehicles of the motor pool to the open-air movie theater.

"And I didn't organize anything," Milo answered indignantly, drawing great agitated sniffs of air in through his hissing, pale, twitching nose. "The Germans have the bridge, and we were going to bomb it, whether I stepped into the picture or not. I just saw a wonderful opportunity to make some profit out of the mission, and I took it. What's so terrible about that?"

"What's so terrible about it? Milo, a man in my tent was killed on that mission before he could even unpack his bags."

"But I didn't kill him."

"You got a thousand dollars extra for it."

"But I didn't kill him. I wasn't even there, I tell you. I was in Barcelona buying olive oil and skinless and boneless sardines, and I've got the purchase orders to prove it. And I didn't get the thousand dollars. That thousand dollars went to the syndicate, and everybody got a share, even you." Milo was appealing to Yossarian from the bottom of his soul. "Look, I didn't start this war, Yossarian, no matter what that lousy Wintergreen is saying. I'm just trying to put it on a businesslike basis. Is anything wrong with that? You know, a thousand dollars ain't such a bad price for a medium bomber and a crew. If I can persuade the Germans to pay me a thousand dollars for every plane they shoot down, why shouldn't I take it?"

"Because you're dealing with the enemy, that's why. Can't you understand that we're fighting a war? People are dying. Look around you, for Christ's sake!"

Milo shook his head with weary forbearance. "And the Germans are not our enemies," he declared. "Oh, I know what you're going to say. Sure, we're at war with them. But the Germans are also members in good standing of the syndicate, and it's my job to protect their rights as shareholders. Maybe they did start the war, and maybe they are killing millions of people, but they pay their bills a lot more promptly than some allies of ours I could name. Don't you understand that I have to respect the sanctity of my contract with Germany? Can't you see it from my point of view?"

"No," Yossarian rebuffed him harshly.

Milo was stung and made no effort to disguise his wounded feelings. It was a muggy, moonlit night filled with gnats, moths, and mosquitoes. Milo lifted his arm suddenly and pointed toward the open-air theater, where the milky, dust-filled beam bursting horizontally from the projector slashed a conelike swath in the blackness and draped in a fluorescent membrane of light the audience tilted on the seats there in hypnotic sags, their faces focused upward toward the aluminized movie screen. Milo's eyes were liquid with integrity, and his artless and uncorrupted face was lustrous with a shining mixture of sweat and insect repellent.

"Look at them," he exclaimed in a voice choked with emotion. "They're my friends, my countrymen, my comrades in arms. A fellow never had a better bunch of buddies. Do you think I'd do a single thing to harm them if I didn't have to? Haven't I got enough on my mind? Can't you see how upset I am already about all that cotton piling up on those piers in Egypt?" Milo's voice splintered into fragments, and he clutched at Yossarian's shirt front as though drowning. His eyes were throbbing visibly like brown caterpillars. "Yossarian, what am I going to do with so much cotton? It's all your fault for letting me buy it."

The cotton was piling up on the piers in Egypt, and nobody wanted any. Milo had never dreamed that the Nile Valley could be so fertile or that there would be no market at all for the crop he had bought. The mess halls in his syndicate would not help; they rose up in uncompromising rebellion against his proposal to tax them on a per capita basis in order to enable each man to own his own share of the Egyptian cotton crop. Even his reliable friends the Germans failed him in this crisis: they preferred ersatz. Milo's mess halls would not even help him store the cotton, and his warehousing costs skyrocketed and contributed to the devastating drain upon his cash reserves. The profits from the Orvieto mission were sucked away. He began writing home for the money he had sent back in better days; soon that was almost gone. And new bales of cotton kept arriving on the wharves at Alexandria every day. Each time he succeeded in dumping some on the world market for a loss it was snapped up by canny Egyptian brokers in the Levant, who sold it back to him at the original contract price, so that he was really worse off than before.

M & M Enterprises verged on collapse. Milo cursed himself hourly for his monumental greed and stupidity in purchasing the entire Egyptian cotton crop, but a contract was a contract and had to be honored, and one night, after a sumptuous evening meal, all Milo's fighters and bombers took off, joined in formation directly overhead and began dropping bombs on the group. He had landed another contract with the Germans, this time to bomb his own outfit. Milo's planes separated in a well-co-ordinated attack and bombed the fuel stocks and the ordnance dump, the repair hangars and the B-25 bombers resting on the lollipop-shaped hardstands at the field. His crews spared the landing strip and the mess halls so that they could land safely when their work was done and enjoy a hot snack before retiring. They bombed with their landing lights on, since no one was shooting back. They bombed all four squadrons, the officers' club and the Group Headquarters building. Men bolted from their tents in sheer terror and did not know in which direction to turn. Wounded soon lay screaming everywhere. A cluster of fragmentation bombs exploded in the yard of the officers' club and punched jagged holes in the side of the wooden building and in the bellies and backs of a row of lieutenants and captains standing at the bar. They doubled over in agony and dropped. The rest of the officers fled toward the two exits in panic and jammed up the doorways like a dense, howling dam of human flesh as they shrank from going farther.

Colonel Cathcart clawed and elbowed his way through the unruly, bewildered mass until he stood outside by himself. He stared up at the sky in stark astonishment and horror. Milo's planes, ballooning serenely in over the blossoming treetops with their bomb bay doors open and wing flaps down and with their monstrous, bug-eyed, blinding, fiercely flickering, eerie landing lights on, were the most apocalyptic sight he had ever beheld. Colonel Cathcart let go a stricken gasp of dismay and hurled himself headlong into his jeep, almost sobbing. He found the gas pedal and the ignition and sped toward the airfield as fast as the rocking car would carry him, his huge flabby hands clenched and bloodless on the wheel or blaring his horn tormentedly. Once he almost killed himself when he swerved with a banshee screech of tires to avoid plowing into a bunch of men running crazily toward the hills in their underwear with their stunned faces down and their thin arms pressed high around their temples as puny shields. Yellow, orange and red fires were burning on both sides of the road. Tents and trees were in flames, and Milo's planes kept coming around interminably with their blinking white landing lights on and their bomb bay doors open. Colonel Cathcart almost turned the jeep over when he slammed the brakes on at the control tower. He leaped from the car while it was still skidding dangerously and hurtled up the flight of steps inside, where three men were busy at the instruments and the controls. He bowled two of them aside in his lunge for the nickel-plated microphone, his eyes glittering wildly and his beefy face contorted with stress. He squeezed the microphone in a bestial grip and began shouting hysterically at the top of his voice,

"Milo, you son of a bitch! Are you crazy? What the hell are you doing? Come down! Come down!"

"Stop hollering so much, will you?" answered Milo, who was standing there right beside him in the control tower with a microphone of his own. "I'm right here." Milo looked at him with reproof and turned back to his work. "Very good, men, very good," he chanted into his microphone. "But I see one supply shed still standing. That will never do, Purvis— I've spoken to you about that kind of shoddy work before. Now, you go right back there this minute and try it again. And this time come in slowly . . . slowly. Haste makes waste, Purvis. Haste makes waste. If I've told you that once, I must have told you that a hundred times. Haste makes waste."

The loud-speaker overhead began squawking. "Milo, this is Alvin Brown. I've finished dropping my bombs. What should I do now?"

"Strafe," said Milo.

"*Strafe?*" Alvin Brown was shocked.

"We have no choice," Milo informed him resignedly. "It's in the contract."

"Oh, okay, then," Alvin Brown acquiesced. "In that case I'll strafe."

This time Milo had gone too far. Bombing his own men and planes was more than even the most phlegmatic observer could stomach, and it looked like the end for him. High-ranking government officials poured in to investigate. Newspapers inveighed against Milo with glaring headlines, and

Congressmen denounced the atrocity in stentorian wrath and clamored for punishment. Mothers with children in the service organized into militant groups and demanded revenge. Not one voice was raised in his defense. Decent people everywhere were affronted, and Milo was all washed up until he opened his books to the public and disclosed the tremendous profit he had made. He could reimburse the government for all the people and property he had destroyed and still have enough money left over to continue buying Egyptian cotton. Everybody, of course, owned a share. And the sweetest part of the whole deal was that there really was no need to reimburse the government at all.

"In a democracy, the government is the people," Milo explained. "We're people, aren't we? So we might just as well keep the money and eliminate the middleman. Frankly, I'd like to see the government get out of war altogether and leave the whole field to private industry. If we pay the government everything we owe it, we'll only be encouraging government control and discouraging other individuals from bombing their own men and planes. We'll be taking away their incentive."

Milo was correct, of course, as everyone soon agreed but a few embittered misfits like Doc Daneeka, who sulked cantankerously and muttered offensive insinuations about the morality of the whole venture until Milo mollified him with a donation, in the name of the syndicate, of a lightweight aluminum collapsible garden chair that Doc Daneeka could fold up conveniently and carry outside his tent each time Chief White Halfoat came inside his tent and carry back inside his tent each time Chief White Holfoat came out. Doc Daneeka had lost his head during Milo's bombardment; instead of running for cover, he had remained out in the open and performed his duty, slithering along the ground through shrapnel, strafing and incendiary bombs like a furtive, wily lizard from casualty to casualty, administering tourniquets, morphine, splints and sulfanilamide with a dark and doleful visage, never saying one word more than he had to and reading in each man's bluing wound a dreadful portent of his own decay. He worked himself relentlessly into exhaustion before the long night was over and came down with a sniffle the next day that sent him hurrying querulously into the medical tent to have his temperature taken by Gus and Wes and to obtain a mustard plaster and vaporizer.

Doc Daneeka tended each moaning man that night with the same glum and profound and introverted grief he showed at the airfield the day of the Avignon mission when Yossarian climbed down the few steps of his plane naked, in a state of utter shock, with Snowden smeared abundantly all over his bare heels and toes, knees, arms and fingers, and pointed inside wordlessly toward where the young radio-gunner lay freezing to death on the floor beside the still younger tail-gunner who kept falling back into a dead faint each time he opened his eyes and saw Snowden dying.

Doc Daneeka draped a blanket around Yossarian's shoulders almost tenderly after Snowden had been removed from the plane and carried into an ambulance on a stretcher. He led Yossarian toward his jeep. McWatt helped, and the three drove in silence to the squadron medical tent, where McWatt and Doc Daneeka guided Yossarian inside to a chair and washed Snowden off him with cold wet balls of absorbent cotton. Doc Daneeka gave him a pill and a shot that put him to sleep for twelve hours. When Yossarian woke up and went to see him, Doc Daneeka gave him another pill and a shot that put him to sleep for another twelve hours. When Yossarian woke up again and went to see him, Doc Daneeka made ready to give him another pill and a shot.

"How long are you going to keep giving me those pills and shots?" Yossarian asked him.

"Until you feel better."

"I feel all right now."

Doc Daneeka's fragile suntanned forehead furrowed with surprise. "Then why don't you put some clothes on? Why are you walking around naked?"

"I don't want to wear a uniform any more."

Doc Daneeka accepted the explanation and put away his hypodermic syringe. "Are you sure you feel all right?"

"I feel fine. I'm just a little logy from all those pills and shots you've been giving me."

Yossarian went about his business with no clothes on all the rest of that day and was still naked late the next morning when Milo, after hunting everywhere else, finally found him sitting up a tree a small distance in back of the quaint little military cemetery at which Snowden was being buried. Milo was dressed in his customary business attire—olive-drab trousers, a fresh olive-drab shirt and tie, with one silver first lieutenant's bar gleaming on the collar, and a regulation dress cap with a stiff leather bill.

"I've been looking all over for you," Milo called up to Yossarian from the ground reproachfully.

"You should have looked for me in this tree," Yossarian answered. "I've been up here all morning."

"Come on down and taste this and tell me if it's good. It's very important."

Yossarian shook his head. He sat nude on the lowest limb of the tree and balanced himself with both hands grasping the bough directly above. He refused to budge, and Milo had no choice but to stretch both arms about the trunk in a distasteful hug and start climbing. He struggled upward clumsily with loud grunts and wheezes, and his clothes were squashed and crooked by the time he pulled himself up high enough to hook a leg over the limb and pause for breath. His dress cap was askew and in danger of falling. Milo caught it just in time when it began slipping. Globules of perspiration glistened like transparent pearls around his mustache and swelled like opaque blisters under his eyes. Yossarian watched him impassively. Cautiously Milo worked himself around in a half circle so that he could face Yossarian. He unwrapped tissue paper from something soft, round and brown and handed it out to Yossarian.

"Please taste this and let me know what you think. I'd like to serve it to the men."

"What is it?" asked Yossarian, and took a big bite.

"Chocolate-covered cotton."

Yossarian gagged convulsively and sprayed his big mouthful of chocolate-covered cotton right out into Milo's face. "Here, take it back!" he spouted angrily. "Jesus Christ! Have you gone crazy? You didn't even take the goddam seeds out."

"Give it a chance, will you?" Milo begged. "It can't be that bad. Is it really that bad?"

"It's even worse."

"But I've got to make the mess halls feed it to the men."

"They'll never be able to swallow it."

"They've got to swallow it," Milo ordained with dictatorial grandeur, and almost broke his neck when he let go with one arm to wave a righteous finger in the air.

"Come on out here," Yossarian invited him. "You'll be much safer, and you can see everything."

Gripping the bough above with both hands, Milo began inching his way out on the limb sideways with utmost care and apprehension. His face was rigid with tension, and he sighed with relief when he found himself seated securely beside Yossarian. He stroked the tree affectionately. "This is a pretty good tree," he observed admiringly with proprietary gratitude.

"It's the tree of life," Yossarian answered, waggling his toes, "and of knowledge of good and evil, too."

Milo squinted closely at the bark and branches. "No it isn't," he replied. "It's a chestnut tree. I ought to know. I sell chestnuts."

"Have it your way."

They sat in the tree without talking for several seconds, their legs dangling and their hands almost straight up on the bough above, the one completely nude but for a pair of crepe-soled sandals, the other completely dressed in a coarse olive-drab woolen uniform with his tie knotted tight. Milo studied Yossarian diffidently through the corner of his eye, hesitating tactfully.

"I want to ask you something," he said at last. "You don't have any clothes on. I don't want to butt in or anything, but I just want to know. Why aren't you wearing your uniform?"

"I don't want to."

Milo nodded rapidly like a sparrow pecking. "I see, I see," he stated quickly with a look of vivid confusion. "I understand perfectly. I heard Appleby and Captain Black say you had gone crazy, and I just wanted to find out." He hesitated politely again, weighing his next question. "Aren't you ever going to put your uniform on again?"

"I don't think so."

Milo nodded with spurious vim to indicate he still understood and then sat silent, ruminating gravely with troubled misgiving. A scarlet-crested bird shot by below, brushing sure dark wings against a quivering bush. Yossarian and Milo were covered in their bower by tissue-thin tiers of sloping green and largely surrounded by other gray chestnut trees and a silver spruce. The sun was high overhead in a vast sapphire-blue sky beaded with low, isolated, puffy clouds of dry and immaculate white. There was no breeze, and the leaves about them hung motionless. The shade was feathery. Everything was at peace but Milo, who straightened suddenly with a muffled cry and began pointing excitedly.

"Look at that!" he exclaimed in alarm. "Look at that! That's a funeral going on down there. That looks like the cemetery. Isn't it?"

Yossarian answered him slowly in a level voice. "They're burying that kid who got killed in my plane over Avignon the other day. Snowden."

"What happened to him?" Milo asked in a voice deadened with awe.

"He got killed."

"That's terrible," Milo grieved, and his large brown eyes filled with tears. "That poor kid. It really is terrible." He bit his trembling lip hard, and his voice rose with emotion when he continued. "And it will get even worse if the mess halls don't agree to buy my cotton. Yossarian, what's the matter with them? Don't they realize it's their syndicate? Don't they know they've all got a share?"

"Did the dead man in my tent have a share?" Yossarian demanded caustically.

"Of course he did," Milo assured him lavishly. "Everybody in the squadron has a share."

"He was killed before he even got into the squadron."

Milo made a deft grimace of tribulation and turned away. "I wish you'd stop picking on me about that dead man in your tent," he pleaded peevishly. "I told you I didn't have anything to do with killing him. Is it my fault that I saw this great opportunity to corner the market on Egyptian cotton and got us into all this trouble? Was I supposed to know there was going to be a glut? I didn't even know what a glut was in those days. An opportunity to corner a market doesn't come along very often, and I was pretty shrewd to grab the chance when I had it." Milo gulped back a moan as he saw six uniformed pallbearers lift the plain pine coffin from the ambulance and set it gently down on the ground beside the yawning gash of the freshly dug grave. "And now I can't get rid of a single penny's worth," he mourned.

Yossarian was unmoved by the fustian charade of the burial ceremony, and by Milo's crushing bereavement. The chaplain's voice floated up to him through the distance tenuously in an unintelligible, almost inaudible monotone, like a gaseous murmur. Yossarian could make out Major Major by his towering and lanky aloofness and thought he recognized Major Danby mopping his brow with a handkerchief. Major Danby had not stopped shaking since his run-in with General Dreedle. There were strands of enlisted men molded in a curve around the three officers, as inflexible as lumps of

wood, and four idle gravediggers in streaked fatigues loung-
ing indifferently on spades near the shocking, incongruous
heap of loose copper-red earth. As Yossarian stared, the chaplain elevated his gaze toward Yossarian beatifically, pressed
his fingers down over his eyeballs in a manner of affliction,
peered upward again toward Yossarian searchingly, and
bowed his head, concluding what Yossarian took to be a
climactic part of the funeral rite. The four men in fatigues
lifted the coffin on slings and lowered it into the grave. Milo
shuddered violently.

"I can't watch it," he cried, turning away in anguish. "I
just can't sit here and watch while those mess halls let my
syndicate die." He gnashed his teeth and shook his head with
bitter woe and resentment. "If they had any loyalty, they
would buy my cotton till it hurts so that they can keep right
on buying my cotton till it hurts them some more. They
would build fires and burn up their underwear and summer
uniforms just to create a bigger demand. But they won't do a
thing. Yossarian, try eating the rest of this chocolate-covered
cotton for me. Maybe it will taste delicious now."

Yossarian pushed his hand away. "Give up, Milo. People
can't eat cotton."

Milo's face narrowed cunningly. "It isn't really cotton,"
he coaxed. "I was joking. It's really cotton candy, delicious
cotton candy. Try it and see."

"Now you're lying."

"I never lie!" Milo rejoindered with proud dignity.

"You're lying now."

"I only lie when it's necessary," Milo explained defen-
sively, averting his eyes for a moment and blinking his lashes
winningly. "This stuff is better than cotton candy, really it is.

It's made out of real cotton. Yossarian, you've got to help me make the men eat it. Egyptian cotton is the finest cotton in the world."

"But it's indigestible," Yossarian emphasized. "It will make them sick, don't you understand? Why don't you try living on it yourself if you don't believe me?"

"I did try," admitted Milo gloomily. "And it made me sick."

The graveyard was yellow as hay and green as cooked cabbage. In a little while the chaplain stepped back, and the beige crescent of human forms began to break up sluggishly, like flotsam. The men drifted without haste or sound to the vehicles parked along the side of the bumpy dirt road. With their heads down disconsolately, the chaplain, Major Major and Major Danby moved toward their jeeps in an ostracized group, each holding himself friendlessly several feet away from the other two.

"It's all over," observed Yossarian.

"It's the end," Milo agreed despondently. "There's no hope left. And all because I left them free to make their own decisions. That should teach me a lesson about discipline the next time I try something like this."

"Why don't you sell your cotton to the government?" Yossarian suggested casually, as he watched the four men in streaked fatigues shoveling heaping bladefuls of the copper-red earth back down inside the grave.

Milo vetoed the idea brusquely. "It's a matter of principle," he explained firmly. "The government has no business in business, and I would be the last person in the world to ever try to involve the government in a business of mine. But the business of government *is* business," he remembered alertly, and continued with elation. "Calvin Coolidge said that, and Calvin Coolidge was a President, so it must be true. And the government does have the responsibility of buying all the Egyptian cotton I've got that no one else wants so that I can make a profit, doesn't it?" Milo's face clouded almost as abruptly, and his spirits descended into a state of sad anxiety. "But how will I get the government to do it?"

"Bribe it," Yossarian said.

"Bribe it!" Milo was outraged and almost lost his balance and broke his neck again. "Shame on you!" he scolded severely, breathing virtuous fire down and upward into his rusty mustache through his billowing nostrils and prim lips. "Bribery is against the law, and you know it. But it's not against the law to make a profit, is it? So it can't be against the law for me to bribe someone in order to make a fair profit, can it? No, of course not!" He fell to brooding again, with a meek, almost pitiable distress. "But how will I know who to bribe?"

"Oh, don't you worry about that," Yossarian comforted him with a toneless snicker as the engines of the jeeps and ambulance fractured the drowsy silence and the vehicles in the rear began driving away backward. "You make the bribe big enough and they'll find you. Just make sure you do everything right out in the open. Let everyone know exactly what you want and how much you're willing to pay for it. The first time you act guilty or ashamed, you might get into trouble."

"I wish you'd come with me," Milo remarked. "I won't feel safe among people who take bribes. They're no better than a bunch of crooks."

"You'll be all right," Yossarian assured him with confidence. "If you run into trouble, just tell everybody that the security of the country requires a strong domestic Egyptian-cotton speculating industry."

"It does," Milo informed him solemnly. "A strong Egyptian-cotton speculating industry means a much stronger America."

"Of course it does. And if that doesn't work, point out the great number of American families that depend on it for income."

"A great many American families do depend on it for income."

"You see?" said Yossarian. "You're much better at it than I am. You almost make it sound true."

"It is true," Milo exclaimed with a strong trace of the old hauteur.

"That's what I mean. You do it with just the right amount of conviction."

"You're sure you won't come with me?"

Yossarian shook his head.

Milo was impatient to get started. He stuffed the remainder of the chocolate-covered cotton ball into his shirt pocket and edged his way back gingerly along the branch to the smooth gray trunk. He threw his arms about the trunk in a generous and awkward embrace and began shinnying down, the sides of his leather-soled shoes slipping constantly so that it seemed many times he would fall and injure himself. Halfway down, he changed his mind and climbed back up. Bits of tree bark stuck to his mustache, and his straining face was flushed with exertion.

"I wish you'd put your uniform on instead of going around naked that way," he confided pensively before he climbed back down again and hurried away. "You might start a trend, and then I'll never get rid of all this goldarned cotton."

JOSEPH HELLER is a leading American novelist whose work has been labelled "black humor." That is, he is not being funny merely to get laughs, but to point out that certain situations are absurd—war, for instance. In contrast to the many blood-and-guts novels that were written after World War II, Mr. Heller's *Catch-22* struck readers as original, honest, and frighteningly funny. It took the normal war novel and turned it upside down. It has been a steady seller since its publication in 1961. In 1969 it was made into a film starring Alan Arkin as Yossarian.

Joseph Heller was born in Brooklyn, New York, in 1923. He graduated from New York University and received a master's degree from Columbia. During World War II he served in the air force. In 1949 he spent a year as a Fulbright scholar at Oxford University in England. After that he taught at Pennsylvania State University and worked for *Time, Look,* and *McCall's* magazines.

Mr. Heller is also the author of a play, *We Bombed in New Haven.* He is married and has two children.

HUMPHREY ELLIS

Statement of Arthur James Wentworth, Bachelor of Arts

My name is Arthur James Wentworth, I am unmarried and I am by profession an assistant master at Burgrove Preparatory School, Wilminster. The Headmaster is the Reverend Gregory Saunders, M.A. He is known to the boys as the Squid—not necessarily, I think, a term of opprobrium. He is a classical scholar of moderate attainments, a generous employer and much given to the use of the expression "The School must come first, Wentworth." I attach no particular meaning to this remark.

At 11:15 on the morning of Saturday, 8th July, I entered Classroom 4 for the purpose of instructing Set IIIA in Algebra. There were present Anderson, Atkins, Clarke, Etheridge, Hillman, Hopgood II, Mason, Otterway, Sapoulos, Trench and Williamson. Heathcote, who has, I am told, a boil, was absent. It should be explained that though I have given these names in the alphabetical order in which they appear in the school list, that is not the order in which the boys were sitting on this occasion. It is the custom at Burgrove for boys to sit according to their position in the previous week's mark-lists. Thus in the front row were seated Etheridge, a most promising mathematician, Hillman, Mason, Otterway and Clarke. Hopgood II, the boy whom I am now accused of assaulting, was in the middle of the second row. The third and last row was shared by Sapoulos, a Greek, and Atkins, a cretin. I do not think these facts have any bearing on anything that is to follow, but I give them for the sake of completeness.

"This morning," I remarked, taking up my Hall and Knight, "we will do problems," and I told them at once that if there was any more of that groaning they would do nothing but problems for the next month. It is my experience, as an assistant-master of some years' standing, that if groaning is not checked immediately it may swell to enormous proportions. I make it my business to stamp on it.

Mason, a fair-haired boy with glasses, remarked when the groaning had died down that it would not be possible to do problems for the next month, and on being asked why not, replied that there were only three weeks more of term. This was true, and I decided to make no reply. He then asked if he could have a mark for that. I said, "No, Mason, you may not," and, taking up my book and a piece of chalk, read out, "I am just half as old as my father and in twenty years I shall

be five years older than he was twenty years ago. How old am
I?" Atkins promptly replied, "Forty-two." I inquired of him
how, unless he was gifted with supernatural powers, he imag-
ined he could produce the answer without troubling to do
any working-out. He said, "I saw it in the *Schools Year-book.*"
This stupid reply caused a great deal of laughter, which I
suppressed.

I should have spoken sharply to Atkins, but at this
moment I noticed that his neighbour Sapoulos, the Greek
boy, appeared to be eating toffee, a practice which is for-
bidden at Burgrove during school hours. I ordered him to
stand up. "Sapoulos," I said, "you are not perhaps quite used
yet to our English ways, and I shall not punish you this time
for your disobedience; but please understand that I will not
have eating in my class. You did not come here to eat but to
learn. If you try hard and pay attention I do not altogether
despair of teaching you something, but if you do not wish to
learn I cannot help you. You might as well go back to your
own country." Mason, without being given permission to
speak, cried excitedly, "He can't, sir. Didn't you know? His
father was chased out of Greece in a revolution or something.
A big man with a black beard chased him for three miles and
he had to escape in a small boat. It's true, sir. You ask him.
Sapoulos got hit on the knee with a brick, didn't you, Sappy?
And his grandmother—at least I think it was his grandmother—"

"That will do, Mason," I said. "Who threw that?"

I am not, I hope, a martinet, but I will not tolerate the
throwing of paper darts or other missiles in my algebra set.
Some of the boys make small pellets out of their blotting
paper and flick them with their garters. This sort of thing has

to be put down with a firm hand or work becomes impossible. I accordingly warned the boy responsible that another offence would mean an imposition. He had the impertinence to ask what sort of an imposition. I said that it would be a pretty stiff imposition, and if he wished to know more exact details he had only to throw another dart to find out. He thereupon threw another dart.

I confess that at this I lost patience and threatened to keep the whole set in during the afternoon if I had any more trouble. The lesson then proceeded.

It was not until I had completed my working out of the problem on the board that I realised I had worked on the assumption—of course ridiculous—that I was *twice* my father's age instead of *half*. This gave the false figure of minus ninety for my own age. Some boy said "Crikey!" I at once whipped round and demanded to know who had spoken. Otterway suggested that it might have been Hopgood II talking in his sleep. I was about to reprimand Otterway for impertinence when I realised that Hopgood actually was asleep and had in fact, according to Williamson, been asleep since the beginning of the period. Mason said, "He hasn't missed much anyway."

I then threw my Hall and Knight. It has been suggested that it was intended to hit Hopgood II. This is false. I never wake up sleeping boys by throwing books at them, as hundreds of old Burgrove boys will be able to testify. I intended to hit Mason, and it was by a mischance which I shall always regret that Hopgood was struck. I have had, as I told my Headmaster, a great deal to put up with from Mason, and no one who knows the boy blames me for the attempt to do him some physical violence. It is indeed an accepted maxim in the

Common Room that physical violence is the only method of dealing with Mason which produces any results; to this the Headmaster some time ago added a rider that the boy be instructed to remove his spectacles before being assaulted. That I forgot to do this must be put down to the natural agitation of a mathematics master caught out in an error. But I blame myself for it.

I do not blame myself for the unfortunate stunning of Hopgood II. It was an accident. I did all I could for the boy when it was discovered (I think by Etheridge) that he had been rendered unconscious. I immediately summoned the Headmaster and we talked the matter over. We agreed that concealment was impossible and that I must give a full account of the circumstances to the police. Meanwhile the work of the school was to go on as usual; Hopgood himself would have wished it. The Headmaster added that in any case the School must come first.

I have made this statement after being duly cautioned, of my own free will and in the presence of witnesses. I have read it through three times with considerable satisfaction, and am prepared to state on oath that it is a true and full account of the circumstances leading up to the accident to Hopgood II. I wish only to add that the boy is now none the worse for the blow, and has indeed shown increased zeal for his studies since the occurrence.

(*Signed*) A. J. WENTWORTH, B.A.

8th July, 1939

HUMPHREY ELLIS is a member of the staff of *Punch*. Mr. Ellis was born in 1907. He was educated at Magdalen College, one of the colleges that make up Oxford University. For two years he was assistant master at Marlborough College, where he may have acquired the experience to write the pathetic story of Arthur James Wentworth. He began contributing to *Punch* in 1931, and became a full-time staff member in 1933. Mr. Ellis also contributes to *The New Yorker* and other American magazines. He presently lives in Somerset, England.

ROBERT BENCHLEY

The Stranger Within Our Gates

One of the problems of child education which is not generally included in books on the subject is the Visiting Schoolmate. By this is meant the little friend whom your child brings home for the holidays. What is to be done with him, the Law reading as it does?

He is usually brought home because his own home is in Nevada, and if he went way out there for Christmas he would no sooner get there than he would have to turn right around and come back—an ideal arrangement on the face of it. But there is something in the idea of a child away from home at Christmas-time that tears at the heart-strings, and little George is received into the bosom of your family with open arms and a slight catch in the throat. Poor little nipper! He must call up his parents by telephone on Christmas Day; they will miss him so. (It later turns out that even when George's parents lived in Philadelphia he spent his vacations with friends, his parents being no fools.)

For the first day George is a model of politeness. "George is a nice boy," you say to your son. "I wish you knew more like him." "George seems to be a very manly little chap for fourteen," your wife says after the boys have gone to bed. "I hope that Bill is impressed." Bill, as a matter of fact, does seem to have caught some of little George's gentility and reserve, and the hope for his future, which had been practically abandoned, is revived again under his schoolmate's influence.

The first indication that George's stay is not going to be a blessing comes at the table, when, with confidence born of one day's association, he announces flatly that he does not eat potatoes, lamb or peas, the main course of the meal consisting of potatoes, lamb and peas. "Perhaps you would like an egg, George?" you suggest. "I hate eggs," says George, looking out the window while he waits for you to hit on something that he does like.

"I'm afraid you aren't going to get much to eat tonight, then, George," you say. "What is there for dessert?"

"A nice bread pudding with raisins," says your wife.

George, at the mention of bread pudding, gives what is known as "the bird," a revolting sound made with the tongue and lower lip. "I can't eat raisins anyway," he adds, to be polite. "They make me come out in a rash."

"Ah-h! The old raisin-rash," you say. "Well, we'll keep

you away from raisins, I guess. And just what is it that you can eat, George? You can tell me. I am your friend."

Under cross-examination it turns out that George can eat beets if they are cooked just right, a rare species of eggplant grown only in Nevada, and all the ice cream in the world. He will also cram down a bit of cake now and then for manners' sake.

All this would not be so bad if it were not for the fact that, coincidentally with refusing the lamb, George criticizes your carving of it. "My father carves lamb across the grain instead of the way you do," he says, a little crossly.

"Very interesting," is your comment.

"My father says that only old ladies carve straight down like that," he goes on.

"Well, well," you say pleasantly between your teeth, "that makes me out sort of an old lady, doesn't it?"

"Yes, sir," says George.

"Perhaps you have a different kind of lamb in Nevada," you suggest, hacking off a large chunk. (You have never carved so badly.) "A kind that feeds on your special kind of eggplant."

"We don't have lamb very often," says George. "Mostly squab and duck."

"You stick to squab and duck, George," you say, "and it will be just dandy for that rash of yours. Here take this and like it!" And you toss him a piece of lamb which oddly enough is later found to have disappeared from his plate.

It also turns out later that George's father can build sailboats, make a monoplane that will really fly, repair a broken buzzer and imitate birds, none of which you can do and none of which you have ever tried to do, having given it to be understood that they *couldn't* be done. You begin to hate George's father almost as much as you do George.

"I suppose your father writes articles for the magazines, too, doesn't he, George?" you ask sarcastically.

"Sure," says George with disdain. "He does that Sundays—Sunday afternoons."

This just about cleans up George so far as you are concerned, but there are still ten more days of vacation. And during these ten days your son Bill is induced by George to experiment with electricity to the extent of blowing out all the fuses in the house and burning the cigarette lighter out of the sedan; he is also inspired to call the cook a German spy who broils babies, to insult several of the neighbors' little girls to the point of tears and reprisals, and to refuse spinach. You know that Bill didn't think of these things himself, as he never could have had the imagination.

On Christmas Day all the little presents that you got for George turn out to be things that he already has, only his are better. He incites Bill to revolt over the question of where the tracks to the electric train are to be placed (George maintaining that in his home they run through his father's bathroom, which is the only sensible place for tracks to run). He breaks several of little Barbara's more fragile presents and says that she broke them herself by not knowing how to work them. And the day ends with George running a high temperature and coming down with mumps, necessitating a quarantine and enforced residence in your house for a month.

This is just a brief summary of the Visiting Schoolmate problem. Granted that every child should have a home to go to at Christmas, could there not be some sort of State subsidy designed to bring their own homes on to such children as are unable to go home themselves? On such a day each home should be a sanctuary, where only members of the tribe can gather and overeat and quarrel. Outsiders just complicate matters, especially when outsiders cannot be spanked.

ROBERT BENCHLEY, with his spectacles, his sparse mustache, and his "unstylish stout" figure, as he called it, looked very much like the hapless hero of his stories. Like W. C. Fields grappling with a hostile pool cue or croquet mallet, Benchley was often attacked by seemingly inanimate objects: "bits of wood and metal, . . . bent on my humiliation and working together . . . have got me licked."

Benchley once jotted down a few helpful biographical notes about himself. He said that he was born on the Isle of Wight in 1807, shipped as a cabin boy on the *Florence J. Marble* in 1815, wrote *A Tale of Two Cities* in 1820, married Princess Anastasie of Portugal in 1831, and was buried in Westminster Abbey in 1871. As a matter of fact, he was born in Worcester, Massachusetts, in 1889. Shortly thereafter he graduated from Harvard, where he was president of the comic magazine, the *Lampoon*. He worked for a publisher and a newspaper, and after World War I he became managing editor of a magazine called *Vanity Fair*. The staff there included Dorothy Parker and a few other wits, and office business often involved burning the editor in effigy or playing a game of charades. Benchley later became drama editor of *Life*, then in its heyday as a humor magazine, where he remained until 1929. In that year he joined *The New Yorker*.

Stage and screen beckoned. In an amateur show, Benchley

first performed his skit called "The Treasurer's Report," a parody that he wrote in a taxi on the way to the first rehearsal. It was a speech in which he garbled figures and shuffled papers in an uneasy manner, and it was a hit. In 1928 he made a short movie of it, the first all-talking film. He made many other movies, and in 1936 won an Oscar for the best short, "How to Sleep." He spent most of his last years in Hollywood. He died in 1945.

An excellent introduction to Robert Benchley is *The Benchley Roundup*. This book was edited by his son, Nathaniel Benchley, and it is illustrated with drawings by *The New Yorker* cartoonist Gluyas Williams. The drawings look very much like Benchley himself.

Throughout his work, Robert Benchley posed vital questions: "Is life made too easy for the youth of today? Are we raising a generation of pampered dawdlers? What is that on your necktie?"

DON MARQUIS

the old trouper

Archy the cockroach, who wrote the following selection on Don Marquis's typewriter, was unable to type capital letters because he was not strong enough to depress the shift key on the typewriter.

i ran onto mehitabel again
last evening
she is inhabiting
a decayed trunk
which lies in an alley
in greenwich village
in company with the
most villainous tom cat
i have ever seen
but there is nothing
wrong about the association
archy she told me

it is merely a plutonic
attachment
and the thing can be
believed for the tom
looks like one of pluto s demons
it is a theatre trunk
archy mehitabel told me
and tom is an old theatre cat
he has given his life
to the theatre
he claims that richard
mansfield once
kicked him out of the way
and then cried because
he had done it and
petted him
and at another time
he says in a case
of emergency
he played a bloodhound
in a production of
uncle tom s cabin
the stage is not what it
used to be tom says
he puts his front paw
on his breast and says
they don t have it any more
they don t have it here
the old troupers are gone
there s nobody can troupe
any more

they are all amateurs nowadays
they haven t got it
here
there are only
five or six of us oldtime
troupers left
this generation does not know
what stage presence is
personality is what they lack
personality
where would they get
the training my old friends
got in the stock companies
i knew mr booth very well
says tom
and a law should be passed
preventing anybody else
from ever playing
in any play he ever
played in
there was a trouper for you
i used to sit on his knee
and purr when i was
a kitten he used to tell me
how much he valued my opinion
finish is what they lack
finish
and they haven t got it
here
and again he laid his paw
on his breast

i remember mr daly very
well too
i was with mr daly s company
for several years
there was art for you
there was team work
there was direction
they knew the theatre
and they all had it
here
for two years mr daly
would not ring up the curtain
unless i was in the
prompter s box
they are amateurs nowadays
rank amateurs all of them
for two seasons i played
the dog in joseph
jefferson s rip van winkle
it is true i never came
on the stage
but he knew i was just off
and it helped him
i would like to see
one of your modern
theatre cats
act a dog so well
that it would convince
a trouper like jo jefferson
but they haven t got it
nowadays

they haven t got it
here
jo jefferson had it he had it
here
i come of a long line
of theatre cats
my grandfather
was with forrest
he had it he was a real trouper
my grandfather said
he had a voice
that used to shake
the ferryboats
on the north river
once he lost his beard
and my grandfather
dropped from the
fly gallery and landed
under his chin
and played his beard
for the rest of the act
you don t see any theatre
cats that could do that
nowadays
they haven t got it they
haven t got it
here
once i played the owl
in modjeska s production
of macbeth
i sat above the castle gate

in the murder scene
and made my yellow
eyes shine through the dusk
like an owl s eyes
modjeska was a real
trouper she knew how to pick
her support i would like
to see any of these modern
theatre cats play the owl s eyes
to modjeska s lady macbeth
but they haven t got it nowadays
they haven t got it
here

mehitabel he says
both our professions
are being ruined
by amateurs

archy

*A biographical sketch of Don Marquis will be found following
the selection "The Case of Doc Green."*

F. SCOTT FITZGERALD

Turkey Remains and How To Inter Them with Numerous Scarce Recipes

At this post holiday season, the refrigerators of the nation are overstuffed with large masses of turkey, the sight of which is calculated to give an adult an attack of dizziness. It seems, therefore, an appropriate time to give the owners the benefit of my experience as an old gourmet, in using this surplus material. Some of the recipes have been in the family for generations. (This usually occurs when rigor mortis sets in.) They were collected over years, from old cook books, yellowed diaries of the Pilgrim Fathers, mail order catalogues, golf-bats and trash cans. Not one but has been tried and proven—there are headstones all over America to testify to the fact.

Very well then: here goes:

1. *Turkey Cocktail:* To one large turkey add one gallon of vermouth and a demijohn of angostura bitters. Shake.

2. *Turkey à la Française:* Take a large ripe turkey, prepare as for basting and stuff with old watches and chains and monkey meat. Proceed as with cottage pudding.

3. *Turkey and Water:* Take one turkey and one pan of water. Heat the latter to the boiling point and then put in the refrigerator. When it has jelled, drown the turkey in it. Eat. In preparing this recipe it is best to have a few ham sandwiches around in case things go wrong.

4. *Turkey Mongole:* Take three butts of salami and a large turkey skeleton, from which the feathers and natural stuffing have been removed. Lay them out on the table and call up some Mongole in the neighborhood to tell you how to proceed from there.

5. *Turkey Mousse:* Seed a large prone turkey, being careful to remove the bones, flesh, fins, gravy, etc. Blow up with a bicycle pump. Mount in becoming style and hang in the front hall.

6. *Stolen Turkey:* Walk quickly from the market, and, if accosted, remark with a laugh that it had just flown into

your arms and you hadn't noticed it. Then drop the turkey with the white of one egg—well, anyhow, beat it.

7. *Turkey à la Crême:* Prepare the crême a day in advance. Deluge the turkey with it and cook for six days over a blast furnace. Wrap in fly paper and serve.

8. *Turkey Hash:* This is the delight of all connoisseurs of the holiday beast, but few understand how really to prepare it. Like a lobster, it must be plunged alive into boiling water, until it becomes bright red or purple or something, and then before the color fades, placed quickly in a washing machine and allowed to stew in its own gore as it is whirled around. Only then is it ready for hash. To hash, take a large sharp tool like a nail-file or, if none is handy, a bayonet will serve the purpose—and then get at it! Hash it well! Bind the remains with dental floss and serve.

9. *Feathered Turkey:* To prepare this, a turkey is necessary and a one pounder cannon to compel anyone to eat it. Broil the feathers and stuff with sage-brush, old clothes, almost anything you can dig up. Then sit down and simmer. The feathers are to be eaten like artichokes (and this is not to be confused with the old Roman custom of tickling the throat).

10. *Turkey à la Maryland:* Take a plump turkey to a barber's and have him shaved, or if a female bird, given a facial and a water wave. Then, before killing him, stuff with old newspapers and put him to roost. He can then be served hot or raw, usually with a thick gravy of mineral oil and

rubbing alcohol. (Note: This recipe was given me by an old black mammy.)

11. *Turkey Remnant:* This is one of the most useful recipes for, though not "chic," it tells us what to do with turkey after the holiday, and how to extract the most value from it. Take the remnants, or, if they have been consumed, take the various plates on which the turkey or its parts have rested and stew them for two hours in milk of magnesia. Stuff with moth-balls.

12. *Turkey with Whiskey Sauce:* This recipe is for a party of four. Obtain a gallon of whiskey, and allow it to age for several hours. Then serve, allowing one quart for each guest. The next day the turkey should be added, little by little, constantly stirring and basting.

13. *For Weddings or Funerals:* Obtain a gross of small white boxes such as are used for bride's cake. Cut the turkey into small squares, roast, stuff, kill, boil, bake and allow to skewer. Now we are ready to begin. Fill each box with a quantity of soup stock and pile in a handy place. As the liquid elapses, the prepared turkey is added until the guests arrive. The boxes delicately tied with white ribbons are then placed in the handbags of the ladies, or in the men's side pockets.

There I guess that's enough turkey talk. I hope I'll never see or hear of another until—well, until next year.

F. SCOTT FITZGERALD is more famous for writing about sadness than for writing jokes. In his novels and short stories, the laughter is often the forced laughter of desperate people. Fitzgerald himself lived with desperation—with success that faded too soon, money that was spent too fast, parties that went on too wildly for too many hours into the night. In 1940 he died in Hollywood, a not-very-successful screenwriter, his best work mostly forgotten. "Poor Scott," Hemingway called him in a story.

But Fitzgerald had a lighthearted side, described by many of his friends. He had a streak of looney Irish nonsense. Often people were offended by his tricks; he was constantly waging food fights in restaurants, swimming in the fountain in front of New York's elegant Plaza hotel or disrupting a Broadway play by laughing loudly at the serious parts. Once he and his friend Ring Lardner forced the cartoonist Rube Goldberg into a barber's chair and cut his hair in outrageously uneven clumps. But somehow people forgave much of his worst behavior. There was always something innocent about Fitzgerald, they said, and besides, he did make you laugh.

Fitzgerald was born in St. Paul, Minnesota, in 1896. He attended Princeton University, where he wrote stories and poetry for the literary magazine and lyrics for the Triangle Club's musical shows. He went on to become one of America's major writers of fiction. His notebooks, in which he jotted down the turkey recipes and some other nonsense, are reprinted in *The Crack-Up*. His novels include *This Side of Paradise* and *The Great Gatsby*, and his short stories are available in a number of collections.

SIR ALAN P. HERBERT

A Criminal Type

To-day I am MAKing aN inno6£vation. as
you mayalready have gessed, I am typlng this
article myself Zz½lnstead of writing it, The
idea is to save time and exvBKpense, also to
demonstyap demonBTrike= =damn, to
demonstrat0 that I can type /ust as well as
any blessedgirl if I give my mInd to iT""
Typling while you compose is realy
extraoraordinarrily easy, though composing
whilr you typE is more difficult. I rather
think my typing style is going to be
different froM my u6sual style, but Idaresay
noone will mind that much. looking back i
see that we made rather a hash of that

awfuul wurd extraorordinnaryk? in the middle
of a woRd like thaton N-e gets quite lost?
2hy do I keep putting questionmarks instead
of fulstopSI wonder.   Now you see i have
put a fulllstop instead Of a question mark
it nevvvver reins but it pours.

the typewriter to me has always been a
mustery£? and even now that I have gained a
perfect mastery over the machine in front of
me i have npt th3 faintest idea hoW it workss%
&or instance why does the thingonthetop the
klnd of lverhead Wailway arrange-ment move
along one pace afterr every word; I haVe exam aaa
ined the mechanism from all points of view but
there seeems to be noreason atall whyit shouould
t£is damn that £, it keeps butting in: it is
Just lik real life.   then there are all kinds
oF attractive devisesand levers andbuttons of
which is amanvel in itself, and does somethI5g
useful without lettin on how it does iT.

Forinstance on this machinE which is Ami/et
a mijge7 imean a mi/dgt, made of alumium,,
and very light sothat you caN CARRY it about
on your £olidays (there is that £ again) and
typeout your poems onthe Moon immmmediately, and
there is onely one lot of keys for capITals and
ordinary latters; when you want todoa Capital
you press down a special key marked cap i mean
CAP with the lefft hand and yo7 press down the
letter withthe other, like that abcd, no,
ABCDEFG . how jolly that looks as a mattr of
fact th is takes a little gettingintoas all the
letters on the keys are printed incapitals so

now and then one forgets topress downthe SPecial
capit al key. not often, though. on the other
hand onceone £as got it down and has written
anice man e in capitals like LLOYdgeORGE IT IS
VERY DIFFICULT TO REmemBER TO PUT IT DOWN AGAIN
ANDTHE N YOU GET THIS SORT OF THING WHICH
SPOILS THE LOOK OF THE HOLE PAGE . or els insted
of preSSing down the key marked CAP onepresses
down the key m arked FIG and then instead of
LLOYDGEORGE you find that you have written
½½96%: 394:3. this is very dissheartening and
£t is no wonder that typists are sooften
sououred in ther youth.

Apart fromthat though the key marked FIG
is rather fun , since you can rite such amusing
things withit, things like % and @ and dear old
& not to mention = and¼ and ¾ and ! ! ! i find
that inones ordinarry (i never get that word
right) cor orrespriden£c one doesnt use expres-
sions like @ @ and %%% nearly enough. type-
writing gives you a new ideaof possibilities o
fthe engli£h language; thE more i look at % the
more beautiful it seems to Be: and like the
simple flowers of england itis per£aps most
beauti£ul when seen in the masss, Look atit

```
% % % % % % % % % % % %
% % % % % % % % % % % %
% % % £ % % % % % % % %
% % % % % % % % % % % %
% % % % % % % % % % £ %
```

how would thatdo for a BAThrooM wallpaper?
it could be produced verery cheaply and itcould
be calld the CHERRYdesigN damn, imeant to put

all that in capitals. iam afraid this articleis
spoilt now but butt bUt curse. But perhaps the
most excitingthing a£out this mac£ine is that
you can by presssing alittle switch suddenly
writein redor green instead of in black; I donvt
understanh how £t is done butit is very jollY?
busisisness men us e the device a great deal
wen writing to their membersof PARLIAment, in
order to emphasasise the pointin wich the£r
in£ustice is worSe than anyone elses
in£ustice. wen they come to WE ARE RUINED they
burst out into red and wen they come to WE w
WOULD remIND YOU tHAT AttHE LAST E£ECTION yoU
UNDERTOOk they burst into GReeN. thei r typists
must enjoy doing those letters. with this arrang
ment of corse one coul d do allkinds of capital
wallpapers. for lnstance wat about a scheme
of red £'s and black %'s and gReen &'s? this
sort of thing

```
£ % £ % £ % £ % £ %
& £ & £ & £ & £ & £
£ % £ % £ % £ % £ %
& £ & £ & £ & £ & £
```

    Manya poor man would be glad to £ave that
in his parLour ratherthan wat he has got now.
of corse, you wont be ab?e to apreciate the
fulll bauty of the design since i underst and
that the retched paper which is going to print
this has no redink and no green inq either; so
you must £ust immagine that the £'s are red and
the &'s are green . it is extroarordinarry (wat a
t erribleword!!!) how backward in MAny waYs

these uptodate papers are wwww¼¼¼¼¼¼¼½=¾ now
how did that happen i wond er; i was experiment-
ing with the BACK SPACE key; if that is wat it
is for i dont thinq i shall use it again. iI
wonder if i am impriving at this½ sometimes i
thinq i am and so metimes i thinq iam not. we
have not had so many £'s lately but i notice
that theere have been one or two misplaced q's &
icannot remember to write i in capital s there
is goes again.

    Of curse the typewriter itself is not
wolly giltless ½ike all mac&ines it has amind
of it sown and is of like passsions with ourselves. i could put that into greek if only
the machine was not so hopelessly MOdern.
it's chief failing is that it cannot write
m'sdecently and instead of h it will keep putting that confounded £. as amatter of fact
ithas been doing m's rather better today butthat
is only its cusssedusssedness and because i have
been opening my shoul ders wenever we have come
to an m; or should it be A m? who can tell;
little peculiuliarities like making indifferent
m's are very important & w£en one is bying a
typewriter one s£ould make careful enquiries
about themc; because it is things of that sort
wich so often give criminals away. there is
notHing a detective likes so much as a type
riter with an idiosxz an idioynq damit an
idiotyncrasy. for instance if i commit a murder
i s£ould not thinq of writing a litter about
it with this of all typewriters becusa because
that fool ofa £ would give me away at once   I

daresay scotland Yard have got specimens of my
trypewriting locked up in some pigeonhole
allready. if they £avent they ought to ; it
ought to be part of my dosossier.

i thinq the place of the hypewriter in ART
is inshufficiently apreciated. Modern art i
understand is chiefly sumbolical expression and
straigt lines. a typwritr can do strait lines
with the under lining mark) and there are few
more atractive symbols thaN the symbols i have
used in this articel ; i merely thro out the
sugestion

I dont tink i shal do many more articles
like this it is tooo much like work? but I am
glad I have got out of that £ habit ;

SIR ALAN P. HERBERT was born in 1890 in England. He was educated at New College, Oxford, and served in World War I with the Royal Naval Division. In 1910 he began to send his writings to *Punch*. Although they were poorly typed, they were funny, and he was invited to join the magazine's staff in 1924. He has also written a number of musical plays. He presently lives in London.

Sir Alan is a lawyer, or barrister-at-law, and much of his humor mocks the complications of the law. He once sent his bank a check, or cheque, as the English say, written on the side of a cow. Accounts of this and other episodes are included in his book *Uncommon Law*.

RING LARDNER

Quadroon

Lardner wrote "Quadroon" partly to make fun of a Broadway hit of the day, a play so long that the audience was given time for a dinner break between acts.

HIC

Part One of *The Quadroon*

CAST

(In Order to Confuse)

CHRISTINE, *his sister, played by Alla Nazimova*
LAVINIA, *her daughter, played by Alice Brady*
CASEY JONES, *a midwife, played by William A. Brady*

SCENE: *A Park Avenue Push-Wagon, Armistice Day, 1860.*

Luncheon Intermission of Half an Hour

The Roth Lunch
127 West Fifty-second Street
November 22, 1931

Special Luncheon, 65 Cents

Chopped Tenderloin Steak
or Calves' Liver and Bacon
Carrots Shoestring Potatoes String Beans
Choice of Desserts
Rice Pudding   Strawberry Tart
Tea, Coffee or Milk.

HAEC

Part Two of *The Quadroon*

CAST

CHRISTINE, *his sister, played by Alice Brady*
LAVINIA, *her daughter, played by Alla Nazimova*
FRANKIE AND JOHNNIE, *played by A. H. Woods*

SCENE: *Department of Plant and Structures. An evening in 1850.*

[CHRISTINE *and* LAVINIA *meet off-stage, dancing.*]
LAVINIA Did you-all evah see me-all in "Hedda Gabler"?

CHRISTINE Does yo'all mean "Hedda Gabler" by William Anthony McGuire?

LAVINIA Yo'all done said zac'ly wot Ah'm drivin' at. How did yo'all lak me?

CHRISTINE Well, Ah seen Mrs. Fiske.

FRANKIE AND JOHNNIE Let's you and I run up to Elizabeth Arden's and free ourselves from fatigue with an Ardena Bath.

Dinner Intermission of One Hour and a Half*
Typical Dinner, $1.50
———

Medaillon of lobster au caviar
Grapefruit
Supreme of fresh fruit, Maraschino
Blue Point oyster cocktail
Fresh shrimp cocktail
or
Cream of lettuce, Parmentier
Clear green turtle, Amontillado

———

(*Choice*)
Filet of sole, Farci Isabella
Broiled Boston scrod, Maître d'Hôtel
Tartelette of Fresh mushrooms,
Lucullus
Country sausages, apple sauce
Breaded spring lamb chop

---

* It will doubtless promote good fellowship and good service if, when entering the hotel's dining-room, you say to the man in charge: "Hello, Maitre d'Hotel."

with Bacon, tomato sauce
Chicken hash au Gratin
Roast sugar cured ham, cider sauce
Omelette Glacé aux Confitures
Cold—Fresh calf's tongue
with chow chow

———

Stewed celery or fresh string beans
Mashed or French fried potatoes
(*Choice*)

Pudding Creole   Coffee éclair
Assorted cakes
Vanilla, raspberry or chocolate
ice cream and cake

———

Delicious apple   Apple pie
French pastry   Coffee, Tea or Milk

Make the Plaza Central
your New York Home
During the
Entire Performance. Ask Arnold.

HOC

Part Three of *The Quadroon*

CAST

LYNN FONTANNE, *a Mrs. Lunt, played by* Grace George
CASEY JONES, *a midwife, played by Bert Lahr*

Frank Case, *proprietor of the Algonquin, played by Alice Brady*

Scene: *Jimmy Walker's Wardrobe Trunk.*

[*The Mayor and the Prince of Wales meet outside the stage door, dancing.*]

THE MAYOR New York is the richest market in the world.

THE PRINCE Not only that, but the New York Theatre Market is an unrivalled concentration of spending power.

THE MAYOR The New York Magazine Program reaches that market exclusively.

FRANK CASE Pardon me, Officer, but can either of you boys play a cellophane?

Passengers will Please not Linger in Washrooms until Other Passengers Have Completed Their Toilets.

HUJUS

Part Four of *The Quadroon*

CAST

CHRISTINE, *her sister, played by Alla Nazimova*
LAVINIA, *their little one, played by Alice Brady*
FRED ASTAIRE, *a hoofer, played by Morris Gest*

Scene: *An ambuscade in the Astor lobby.*

[FRED *and* LAVINIA *dance.*]

LAVINIA The minute you try Pebeco Tooth Paste you know by its "bitey" tang that here is a tooth paste that really "gets somewheres."
FRED Will you love me always?
LAVINIA As long as you keep kissable.
      [*She kills him with an oyster fork.*]

(*Leave your ticket check with an usher and your car
will come right to your seat.*)

   A biographical sketch of Ring Lardner will be found fol-lowing the selection "I Can't Breathe."

JAMES THURBER

You Could Look It Up

It all begun when we dropped down to C'lumbus, Ohio, from Pittsburgh to play a exhibition game on our way out to St. Louis. It was gettin' on into September, and though we'd been leadin' the league by six, seven games most of the season, we was now in first place by a margin you could 'a' got it into the eye of a thimble, bein' only a half a game ahead of St. Louis. Our slump had given the boys the leapin' jumps, and they was like a bunch a old ladies at a lawn fete with a thunderstorm comin' up, runnin' around snarlin' at each other, eatin' bad and sleepin' worse, and battin' for a team average of maybe .186. Half the time nobody'd speak to nobody else, without it was to bawl 'em out.

Squawks Magrew was managin' the boys at the time, and

he was darn near crazy. They called him "Squawks" 'cause when things was goin' bad he lost his voice, or perty near lost it, and squealed at you like a little girl you stepped on her doll or somethin'. He yelled at everybody and wouldn't listen to nobody, without maybe it was me. I'd been trainin' the boys for ten year, and he'd take more lip from me than from anybody else. He knowed I was smarter'n him, anyways, like you're goin' to hear.

This was thirty, thirty-one year ago; you could look it up, 'cause it was the same year C'lumbus decided to call itself the Arch City, on account of a lot of iron arches with electric-light bulbs into 'em which stretched acrost High Street. Thomas Albert Edison sent 'em a telegram, and they was speeches and maybe even President Taft opened the celebration by pushin' a button. It was a great week for the Buckeye capital, which was why they got us out there for this exhibition game.

Well, we just lose a double-header to Pittsburgh, 11 to 5 and 7 to 3, so we snarled all the way to C'lumbus, where we put up at the Chittaden Hotel, still snarlin'. Everybody was tetchy, and when Billy Klinger took a sock at Whitey Cott at breakfast, Whitey throwed marmalade all over his face.

"Blind each other, whatta I care?" says Magrew. "You can't see nothin' anyways."

C'lumbus win the exhibition game, 3 to 2, whilst Magrew set in the dugout, mutterin' and cursin' like a fourteen-year-old Scotty. He bad-mouthed everybody on the ball club and he bad-mouthed everybody offa the ball club, includin' the Wright brothers, who, he claimed, had yet to build a airship big enough for any of our boys to hit it with a ball bat.

"I wisht I was dead," he says to me. "I wisht I was in heaven with the angels."

I told him to pull hisself together, 'cause he was drivin' the boys crazy, the way he was goin' on, sulkin' and badmouthin' and whinin'. I was older'n he was and smarter'n he was, and he knowed it. I was ten times smarter'n he was about this Pearl du Monville, first time I ever laid eyes on the little guy, which was one of the saddest days of my life.

Now, most people name of Pearl is girls, but this Pearl du Monville was a man, if you could call a fella a man who was only thirty-four, thirty-five inches high. Pearl du Monville was a midget. He was part French and part Hungarian, and maybe even part Bulgarian or somethin'. I can see him now, a sneer on his little pushed-in pan, swingin' a bamboo cane and smokin' a big cigar. He had a gray suit with a big black check into it, and he had a gray felt hat with one of them rainbow-colored hatbands onto it, like the young fellas wore in them days. He talked like he was talkin' into a tin can, but he didn't have no foreign accent. He might a been fifteen or he might a been a hundred, you couldn't tell. Pearl du Monville.

After the game with C'lumbus, Magrew headed straight for the Chittaden bar—the train for St. Louis wasn't goin' for three, four hours—and there he set, drinkin' rye and talkin' to this bartender.

"How I pity me, brother," Magrew was tellin' this bartender. "How I pity me." That was alwuz his favorite tune. So he was settin' there, tellin' this bartender how heartbreakin' it was to be manager of a bunch a blindfolded circus clowns, when up pops this Pearl du Monville outa nowheres.

It give Magrew the leapin' jumps. He thought at first maybe the D.T.'s had come back on him; he claimed he'd had 'em once, and little guys had popped up all around him, wearin' red, white and blue hats.

"Go on, now!" Magrew yells. "Get away from me!"

But the midget clumb up on a chair acrost the table from Magrew and says, "I seen that game today, Junior, and you ain't got no ball club. What you got there, Junior," he says, "is a side show."

"Whatta ya mean, 'Junior'?" says Magrew, touchin' the little guy to satisfy hisself he was real.

"Don't pay him no attention, mister," says the bartender. "Pearl calls everybody 'Junior,' 'cause it alwuz turns out he's a year older'n anybody else."

"Yeh?" says Magrew. "How old is he?"

"How old are you, Junior?" says the midget.

"Who, me? I'm fifty-three," says Magrew.

"Well, I'm fifty-four," says the midget.

Magrew grins and asts him what he'll have, and that was the beginnin' of their beautiful friendship, if you don't care what you say.

Pearl du Monville stood up on his chair and waved his cane around and pretended like he was ballyhooin' for a circus. "Right this way, folks!" he yells. "Come on in and see the greatest collection of freaks in the world! See the armless pitchers, see the eyeless batters, see the infielders with five thumbs!" and on and on like that, feedin' Magrew gall and handin' him a laugh at the same time, you might say.

You could hear him and Pearl du Monville hootin' and hollerin' and singin' way up to the fourth floor of the Chittaden, where the boys was packin' up. When it come time to go to the station, you can imagine how disgusted we was when we crowded into the doorway of that bar and seen them two singin' and goin' on.

"Well, well, well," says Magrew, lookin' up and spottin' us. "Look who's here. . . . Clowns, this is Pearl du Monville, a monseer of the old, old school. . . . Don't shake hands with 'em, Pearl, 'cause their fingers is made of chalk and would bust right off in your paws," he says, and he starts guffawin' and Pearl starts titterin' and we stand there givin' 'em the iron eye, it bein' the lowest ebb a ball-club manager'd got hisself down to since the national pastime was started.

Then the midget begun givin' us the ballyhoo. "Come on in!" he says, wavin' his cane. "See the legless base runners, see the outfielders with the butter fingers, see the southpaw with the arm of a little chee-ild!"

Then him and Magrew begun to hoop and holler and nudge each other till you'd of thought this little guy was the funniest guy than even Charlie Chaplin. The fellas filed outa the bar without a word and went on up to the Union Depot, leavin' me to handle Magrew and his new-found crony.

Well, I got 'em outa there finely. I had to take the little guy along, 'cause Magrew had a holt onto him like a vise and I couldn't pry him loose.

"He's comin' along as masket," says Magrew, holdin' the midget in the crouch of his arm like a football. And come along he did, hollerin' and protestin' and beatin' at Magrew with his little fists.

"Cut it out, will ya, Junior?" the little guy kept whinin'. "Come on, leave a man loose, will ya, Junior?"

But Junior kept a holt onto him and begun yellin', "See

the guys with the glass arm, see the guys with the cast-iron brains, see the fielders with the feet on their wrists!"

So it goes, right through the whole Union Depot, with people starin' and catcallin', and he don't put the midget down till he gets him through the gates.

"How'm I goin' to go along without no toothbrush?" the midget asts. "What'm I goin' to do without no other suit?" he says.

"Doc here," says Magrew, meanin' me—"doc here will look after you like you was his own son, won't you, doc?"

I give him the iron eye, and he finely got on the train and prob'ly went to sleep with his clothes on.

This left me alone with the midget. "Lookit," I says to him. "Why don't you go on home now? Come mornin', Magrew'll forget all about you. He'll prob'ly think you was somethin' he seen in a nightmare maybe. And he ain't goin' to laugh so easy in the mornin', neither," I says. "So why don't you go on home?"

"Nix," he says to me. "Skiddoo," he says, "twenty-three for you," and he tosses his cane up into the vestibule of the coach and clam'ers on up after it like a cat. So that's the way Pearl du Monville come to go to St. Louis with the ball club.

I seen 'em first at breakfast the next day, settin' opposite each other; the midget playin' "Turkey in the Straw" on a harmonium and Magrew starin' at his eggs and bacon like they was a uncooked bird with its feathers still on.

"Remember where you found this?" I says, jerkin' my thumb at the midget. "Or maybe you think they come with breakfast on these trains," I says, bein' a good hand at turnin' a sharp remark in them days.

The midget puts down the harmonium and turns on me. "Sneeze," he says; "your brains is dusty." Then he snaps a couple drops of water at me from a tumbler. "Drown," he says, tryin' to make his voice deep.

Now, both them cracks is Civil War cracks, but you'd of thought they was brand new and the funniest than any crack Magrew'd ever heard in his whole life. He started hoopin' and hollerin', and the midget started hoopin' and hollerin', so I walked on away and set down with Bugs Courtney and Hank Metters, payin' no attention to this weak-minded Damon and Phidias acrost the aisle.

Well, sir, the first game with St. Louis was rained out, and there we was facin' a double-header next day. Like maybe I told you, we lost the last three double-headers we play, makin' maybe twenty-five errors in the six games, which is all right for the intimates of a school for the blind, but is disgraceful for the world's champions. It was too wet to go to the zoo, and Magrew wouldn't let us go to the movies, 'cause they flickered so bad in them days. So we just set around, stewin' and frettin'.

One of the newspaper boys come over to take a pitture of Billy Klinger and Whitey Cott shakin' hands—this reporter'd heard about the fight—and whilst they was standin' there, toe to toe, shakin' hands, Billy give a back lunge and a jerk, and throwed Whitey over his shoulder into a corner of the room, like a sack a salt. Whitey come back at him with a chair, and Bethlehem broke loose in that there room. The camera was tromped to pieces like a berry basket. When we finely got 'em pulled apart, I heard a laugh, and there was Magrew and the midget standin' in the door and givin' us the iron eye.

"Wrasslers," says Magrew, cold-like, "that's what I got for a ball club, Mr. Du Monville, wrasslers—and not very good wrasslers at that, you ast me."

"A man can't be good at everythin'," says Pearl, "but he oughta be good at somethin'."

This sets Magrew guffawin' again, and away they go, the midget taggin' along by his side like a hound dog and handin' him a fast line of so-called comic cracks.

When we went out to face that battlin' St. Louis club in a double-header the next afternoon, the boys was jumpy as tin toys with keys in their back. We lose the first game, 7 to 2, and are trailin', 4 to 0, when the second game ain't but ten minutes old. Magrew set there like a stone statue, speakin' to nobody. Then, in their half a the fourth, somebody singled to center and knocked in two more runs for St. Louis.

That made Magrew squawk. "I wisht one thing," he says. "I wisht I was manager of a old ladies' sewin' circus 'stead of a ball club."

"You are, Junior, you are," says a familyer and disagreeable voice.

It was that Pearl du Monville again, poppin' up outa nowheres, swingin' his bamboo cane and smokin' a cigar that's three sizes too big for his face. By this time we'd finely got the other side out, and Hank Metters slithered a bat acrost the ground, and the midget had to jump to keep both his ankles from bein' broke.

I thought Magrew'd bust a blood vessel. "You hurt Pearl and I'll break your neck!" he yelled.

Hank muttered somethin' and went on up to the plate and struck out.

We managed to get a couple runs acrost in our half a the

sixth, but they come back with three more in their half a the seventh, and this was too much for Magrew.

"Come on, Pearl," he says. "We're gettin' outa here."

"Where you think you're goin'?" I ast him.

"To the lawyer's again," he says cryptly.

"I didn't know you'd been to the lawyer's once, yet," I says.

"Which that goes to show how much you don't know," he says.

With that, they was gone, and I didn't see 'em the rest of the day, nor know what they was up to, which was a God's blessin'. We lose the nightcap, 9 to 3, and that puts us into second place plenty, and as low in our mind as a ball club can get.

The next day was a horrible day, like anybody that lived through it can tell you. Practice was just over and the St. Louis club was takin' the field, when I hears this strange sound from the stands. It sounds like the nervous whickerin' a horse gives when he smells somethin' funny on the wind. It was the fans ketchin' sight of Pearl du Monville, like you have prob'ly guessed. The midget had popped up onto the field all dressed up in a minacher club uniform, sox, cap, little letters sewed onto his chest, and all. He was swingin' a kid's bat and the only thing kept him from lookin' like a real ballplayer seen through the wrong end of a microscope was this cigar he was smokin'.

Bugs Courtney reached over and jerked it outa his mouth and throwed it away. "You're wearin' that suit on the playin' field," he says to him, severe as a judge. "You go insultin' it and I'll take you out to the zoo and feed you to the bears."

Pearl just blowed some smoke at him which he still has in his mouth.

Whilst Whitey was foulin' off four or five prior to strikin' out, I went on over to Magrew. "If I was as comic as you," I says, "I'd laugh myself to death," I says. "Is that any way to treat the uniform, makin' a mockery out of it?"

"It might surprise you to know I ain't makin' no mockery outa the uniform," says Magrew. "Pearl du Monville here has been made a bone-of-fida member of this so-called ball club. I fixed it up with the front office by long-distance phone."

"Yeh?" I says. "I can just hear Mr. Dillworth or Bart Jenkins agreein' to hire a midget for the ball club. I can just hear 'em." Mr. Dillworth was the owner of the club and Bart Jenkins was the secretary, and they never stood for no monkey business. "May I be so bold as to inquire," I says, "just what you told 'em?"

"I told 'em," he says, "I wanted to sign up a guy they ain't no pitcher in the league can strike him out."

"Uh-huh," I says, "and did you tell 'em what size of a man he is?"

"Never mind about that," he says. "I got papers on me, made out legal and proper, constitutin' one Pearl du Monville a bone-of-fida member of this former ball club. Maybe that'll shame them big babies into gettin' in there and swingin', knowin' I can replace any one of 'em with a midget, if I have a mind to. A St. Louis lawyer I seen twice tells me it's all legal and proper."

"A St. Louis lawyer would," I says, "seein' nothin' could make him happier than havin' you makin' a mockery outa this one-time baseball outfit," I says.

Well, sir, it'll all be there in the papers of thirty, thirty-one year ago, and you could look it up. The game went along without no scorin' for seven innings, and since they ain't nothin' much to watch but guys poppin' up or strikin' out, the fans pay most of their attention to the goin's-on of Pearl du Monville. He's out there in front a the dugout, turnin' handsprings, balancin' his bat on his chin, walkin' a imaginary line, and so on. The fans clapped and laughed at him, and he ate it up.

So it went up to the last a the eighth, nothin' to nothin', not more'n seven, eight hits all told, and no errors on neither side. Our pitcher gets the first two men out easy in the eighth. Then up come a fella name of Porter or Billings, or some such name, and he lammed one up against the tobacco sign for three bases. The next guy up slapped the first ball out into left for a base hit, and in come the fella from third for the only run of the ball game so far. The crowd yelled, the look a death come onto Magrew's face again, and even the midget quit his tom-foolin'. Their next man fouled out back a third, and we come up for our last bats like a bunch a schoolgirls steppin' into a pool of cold water. I was lower in my mind than I'd been since the day in Nineteen-four when Chesbro throwed the wild pitch in the ninth inning with a man on third and lost the pennant for the Highlanders. I knowed something just as bad was goin' to happen, which shows I'm a clairvoyun, or was then.

When Gordy Mills hit out to second, I just closed my eyes. I opened 'em up again to see Dutch Muller standin' on second, dustin' off his pants, him havin' got his first hit in maybe twenty times to the plate. Next up was Harry Loesing, battin' for our pitcher, and he got a base on balls, walkin' on a fourth one you could a combed your hair with.

Then up come Whitey Cott, our lead-off man. He crotches down in what was prob'ly the most fearsome stanch in organized ball, but all he can do is pop out to short. That brung up Billy Klinger, with two down and a man on first and second. Billy took a cut at one you could a knocked a plug hat offa this here Carnera with it, but then he gets sense enough to wait 'em out, and finely he walks, too, fillin' the bases.

Yes, sir, there you are; the tyin' run on third and the winnin' run on second, first a the ninth, two men down, and Hank Metters comin' to the bat. Hank was built like a Pope-Hartford and he couldn't run no faster'n President Taft, but he had five home runs to his credit for the season, and that wasn't bad in them days. Hank was still hittin' better'n anybody else on the ball club, and it was mighty heartenin', seein' him stridin' up towards the plate. But he never got there.

"Wait a minute!" yells Magrew, jumpin' to his feet. "I'm sendin' in a pinch hitter!" he yells.

You could a heard a bomb drop. When a ball-club manager says he's sendin' in a pinch hitter for the best batter on the club, you know and I know and everybody knows he's lost his holt.

"They're goin' to be sendin' the funny wagon for you, if you don't watch out," I says, grabbin' a holt of his arm.

But he pulled away and run out towards the plate, yellin', "Du Monville battin' for Metters!"

All the fellas begun squawlin' at once, except Hank, and he just stood there starin' at Magrew like he'd gone crazy and was claimin' to be Ty Cobb's grandma or somethin'. Their pitcher stood out there with his hands on his hips and a disagreeable look on his face, and the plate umpire told Magrew to go on and get a batter up. Magrew told him again Du Monville was battin' for Metters, and the St. Louis manager finely got the idea. It brung him outa his dugout, howlin' and bawlin' like he'd lost a female dog and her seven pups.

Magrew pushed the midget towards the plate and he says to him, he says, "Just stand up there and hold that bat on your shoulder. They ain't a man in the world can throw three strikes in there 'fore he throws four balls!" he says.

"I get it, Junior!" says the midget. "He'll walk me and force in the tyin' run!" And he starts on up to the plate as cocky as if he was Willie Keeler.

I don't need to tell you Bethlehem broke loose on that there ball field. The fans got onto their hind legs, yellin' and whistlin', and everybody on the field begun wavin' their arms and hollerin' and shovin'. The plate umpire stalked over to Magrew like a traffic cop, waggin' his jaw and pointin' his finger, and the St. Louis manager kept yellin' like his house was on fire. When Pearl got up to the plate and stood there, the pitcher slammed his glove down onto the ground and started stompin' on it, and they ain't nobody can blame him. He's just walked two normal-sized human bein's, and now here's a guy up to the plate they ain't more'n twenty inches between his knees and his shoulders.

The plate umpire called in the field umpire, and they talked a while, like a couple doctors seein' the bucolic plague or somethin' for the first time. Then the plate umpire come over to Magrew with his arms folded acrost his chest, and he told him to go on and get a batter up, or he'd forfeit the game to St. Louis. He pulled out his watch, but somebody batted it outa his hand in the scufflin', and I thought there'd be a free-for-all, with everybody yellin' and shovin' except Pearl du Monville, who stood up at the plate with his little bat on his shoulder, not movin' a muscle.

Then Magrew played his ace. I seen him pull some papers outa his pocket and show 'em to the plate umpire. The umpire begun lookin' at 'em like they was bills for somethin' he not only never bought it, he never even heard of it. The other umpire studied 'em like they was a death warren, and all this time the St. Louis manager and the fans and the players is yellin' and hollerin'.

Well, sir, they fought about him bein' a midget, and they fought about him usin' a kid's bat, and they fought about where'd he been all season. They was eight or nine rule books brung out and everybody was thumbin' through 'em, tryin' to find out what it says about midgets, but it don't say nothin' about midgets, 'cause this was somethin' never'd come up in the history of the game before, and nobody'd ever dreamed about it, even when they has nightmares. Maybe you can't send no midgets in to bat nowadays, 'cause the old game's changed a lot, mostly for the worst, but you could then, it turned out.

The plate umpire finely decided the contrack papers was all legal and proper, like Magrew said, so he waved the St. Louis players back to their places and he pointed his finger at their manager and told him to quit hollerin' and get on back in the dugout. The manager says the game is percedin' under protest, and the umpire bawls, "Play ball!" over 'n' above the yellin' and booin', him havin' a voice like a hog-caller.

The St. Louis pitcher picked up his glove and beat at it
with his fist six or eight times, and then got set on the mound
and studied the situation. The fans realized he was really
goin' to pitch to the midget, and they went crazy, hoopin'
and hollerin' louder'n ever, and throwin' pop bottles and
hats and cushions down onto the field. It took five, ten
minutes to get the fans quieted down again, whilst our fellas
that was on base set down on the bags and waited. And Pearl
du Monville kept standin' up there with the bat on his
shoulder, like he'd been told to.

So the pitcher starts studyin' the setup again, and you
got to admit it was the strangest setup in a ball game since the
players cut off their beards and begun wearin' gloves. I wisht
I could call the pitcher's name—it wasn't old Barney Pelty
nor Nig Jack Powell nor Harry Howell. He was a big right-
hander, but I can't call his name. You could look it up. Even
in a crotchin' position, the ketcher towers over the midget
like the Washington Monument.

The plate umpire tries standin' on his tiptoes, then he
tries crotchin' down, and he finely gets hisself into a stanch
nobody'd ever seen on a ball field before, kinda squattin'
down on his hanches.

Well, the pitcher is sore as a old buggy horse in fly time.
He slams in the first pitch, hard and wild, and maybe two
foot higher'n the midget's head.

"Ball one!" hollers the umpire over 'n' above the racket,
'cause everybody is yellin' worsten ever.

The ketcher goes on out towards the mound and talks to
the pitcher and hands him the ball. This time the big right-
hander tried a undershoot, and it comes in a little closer,
maybe no higher'n a foot, foot and a half above Pearl's head.

It would a been a strike with a human bein' in there, but the umpire's got to call it, and he does.

"Ball two!" he bellers.

The ketcher walks on out to the mound again, and the whole infield comes over and gives advice to the pitcher about what they'd do in a case like this, with two balls and no strikes on a batter that oughta be in a bottle of alcohol 'stead of up there at the plate in a big-league game between the teams that is fightin' for first place.

For the third pitch, the pitcher stands there flatfooted and tosses up the ball like he's playin' ketch with a little girl.

Pearl stands there motionless as a hitchin' post, and the ball comes in big and slow and high—high for Pearl, that is, it bein' about on a level with his eyes, or a little higher'n a grown man's knees.

They ain't nothin' else for the umpire to do, so he calls, "Ball three!"

Everybody is onto their feet, hoopin' and hollerin', as the pitcher sets to throw ball four. The St. Louis manager is makin' signs and faces like he was a contorturer, and the infield is givin' the pitcher some more advice about what to do this time. Our boys who was on base stick right onto the bag, runnin' no risk of bein' nipped for the last out.

Well, the pitcher decides to give him a toss again, seein' he come closer with that than with a fast ball. They ain't nobody ever seen a slower ball throwed. It come in big as a balloon and slower'n any ball ever throwed before in the major leagues. It come right in over the plate in front of Pearl's chest, lookin' prob'ly big as a full moon to Pearl. They ain't never been a minute like the minute that followed since the United States was founded by the Pilgrim grandfathers.

Pearl du Monville took a cut at that ball, and he hit it! Magrew give a groan like a poleaxed steer as the ball rolls out in front a the plate into fair territory.

"Fair ball!" yells the umpire, and the midget starts runnin' for first, still carryin' that little bat, and makin' maybe ninety foot an hour. Bethlehem breaks loose on that ball field and in them stands. They ain't never been nothin' like it since creation was begun.

The ball's rollin' slow, on down towards third, goin' maybe eight, ten foot. The infield comes in fast and our boys break from their bases like hares in a brush fire. Everybody is standin' up, yellin' and hollerin', and Magrew is tearin' his hair outa his head, and the midget is scamperin' for first with all the speed of one of them little dashhounds carryin' a satchel in his mouth.

The ketcher gets to the ball first, but he boots it on out past the pitcher's box, the pitcher fallin' on his face tryin' to stop it, the shortstop sprawlin' after it full length and zaggin' it on over towards the second baseman, whilst Muller is scorin' with the tyin' run and Loesing is roundin' third with the winnin' run. Ty Cobb could a made a three-bagger outa that bunt, with everybody fallin' over theirself tryin' to pick the ball up. But Pearl is still maybe fifteen, twenty feet from the bag, toddlin' like a baby and yeepin' like a trapped rabbit, when the second baseman finely gets a holt of that ball and slams it over to first. The first baseman ketches it and stomps on the bag, the base umpire waves Pearl out, and there goes your old ball game, the craziest ball game ever played in the history of the organized world.

Their players start runnin' in, and then I see Magrew. He starts after Pearl, runnin' faster'n any man ever run before. Pearl sees him comin' and runs behind the base umpire's legs and gets a holt onto 'em. Magrew comes up, pantin' and roarin', and him and the midget plays ring-around-a-rosy with the umpire, who keeps shovin' at Magrew with one hand and tryin' to slap the midget loose from his legs with the other.

Finely Magrew ketches the midget, who is still yeepin' like a stuck sheep. He gets holt of that little guy by both his ankles and starts whirlin' him round and round his head like Magrew was a hammer thrower and Pearl was the hammer. Nobody can stop him without gettin' their head knocked off, so everybody just stands there and yells. Then Magrew lets the midget fly. He flies on out towards second, high and fast, like a human home run, headed for the soap sign in center field.

Their shortstop tries to get to him, but he can't make it, and I knowed the little fella was goin' to bust to pieces like a dollar watch on a asphalt street when he hit the ground. But it so happens their center fielder is just crossin' second, and he starts runnin' back, tryin' to get under the midget, who had took to spiralin' like a football 'stead of turnin' head over foot, which give him more speed and more distance.

I know you never seen a midget ketched, and you prob'ly never even seen one throwed. To ketch a midget that's been throwed by a heavy-muscled man and is flyin' through the air, you got to run under him and with him and pull your hands and arms back and down when you ketch him, to break the compact of his body, or you'll bust him in two like a matchstick. I seen Bill Lange and Willie Keeler and Tris Speaker make some wonderful ketches in my day, but I never seen nothin' like that center fielder. He goes back and back and still further back and he pulls that midget down outa the air like he was liftin' a sleepin' baby from a cradle. There wasn't a bruise onto him, only his face was the color of cat's meat and he ain't got no air in his chest. In his excitement, the base umpire, who was runnin' back with the center fielder when he ketched Pearl, yells, "Out!" and that give hysteries to the Bethlehem which was ragin' like Niagry on that ball field.

Everybody was hoopin' and hollerin' and yellin' and runnin', with the fans swarmin' onto the field, and the cops tryin' to keep order, and some guys laughin' and some of the women fans cryin', and six or eight of us holdin' onto Magrew to keep him from gettin' at that midget and finishin' him off. Some of the fans picks up the St. Louis pitcher and the center fielder, and starts carryin' 'em around on their shoulders, and they was the craziest goin's-on knowed to the history of organized ball on this side of the 'Lantic Ocean.

I seen Pearl du Monville strugglin' in the arms of a lady fan with a ample bosom, who was laughin' and cryin' at the same time, and him beatin' at her with his little fists and bawlin' and yellin'. He clawed his way loose finely and disappeared in the forest of legs which made that ball field look like it was Coney Island on a hot summer's day.

That was the last I ever seen of Pearl du Monville. I never seen hide nor hair of him from that day to this, and neither did nobody else. He just vanished into the thin of the air, as the fella says. He was ketched for the final out of the ball game and that was the end of him, just like it was the end of the ball game, you might say, and also the end of our losin' streak, like I'm goin' to tell you.

That night we piled onto a train for Chicago, but we wasn't snarlin' and snappin' any more. No, sir, the ice was finely broke and a new spirit come into that ball club. The old zip come back with the disappearance of Pearl du Monville out back a second base. We got to laughin' and talkin' and kiddin' together, and 'fore long Magrew was laughin' with us. He got a human look onto his pan again, and he quit whinin' and complainin' and wishtin' he was in heaven with the angels.

Well, sir, we wiped up that Chicago series, winnin' all four games, and makin' seventeen hits in one of 'em. Funny thing was, St. Louis was so shook up by that last game with us, they never did hit their stride again. Their center fielder took to misjudgin' everything that come his way, and the rest a the fellas followed suit, the way a club'll do when one guy blows up.

'Fore we left Chicago, I and some of the fellas went out and bought a pair of them little baby shoes, which we had 'em golded over and give 'em to Magrew for a souvenir, and he took it all in good spirit. Whitey Cott and Billy Klinger made up and was fast friends again, and we hit our home lot like a ton of dynamite and they was nothin' could stop us from then on.

I don't recollect things as clear as I did thirty, forty year ago. I can't read no fine print no more, and the only person I got to check with on the golden days of the national pastime, as the fella says, is my friend, old Milt Kline, over in Springfield, and his mind ain't as strong as it once was.

He gets Rube Waddell mixed up with Rube Marquard,

for one thing, and anybody does that oughta be put away where he won't bother nobody. So I can't tell you the exact margin we win the pennant by. Maybe it was two and a half games, or maybe it was three and a half. But it'll all be there in the newspapers and record books of thirty, thirty-one year ago and, like I was sayin', you could look it up.

JAMES THURBER was born in Columbus, Ohio, in 1894. As a boy he was blinded in one eye while playing Indians, and for the rest of his life he struggled against increasing blindness in the other. After a while he had to draw with heavy black crayon on large sheets of paper. By 1947 he was no longer able to draw at all, but he continued to write in his lively way until his death in 1961.

Thurber went to Ohio State University. He worked on the *Daily Lantern* there and then as a newspaper reporter in Columbus, Paris, and New York, learning to "get it and write it and put a headline on it." In 1927 E. B. White took him to meet *The New Yorker's* editor, Harold Ross. Ross was always looking for a "miracle man" to organize the office as managing editor. He instantly hired Thurber for the job, but Thurber couldn't perform miracles any more than anyone else could, so he "made deliberate mistakes" and got himself demoted. For the next eight years he was a reporter and writer for the magazine's "Talk of the Town" section. He later wrote for almost every other department, and even covered tennis for several years.

Thurber called himself a "cartoonist, writer, and playwright," in that order. He collaborated with E. B. White on *Is Sex Necessary?* from which the selection in this book, "What Should Children Tell Parents?" is taken. White decided that

Thurber should illustrate the book. One day the two writers showed a batch of Thurber drawings to the book's publisher. After a long silence, the publisher said weakly, "I gather these are a rough idea of the kind of illustrations you want some artist to do?" White shook his head. "These are the drawings that go into the book," he said firmly. There was an argument, but the drawings were published and the book was a success.

In 1930 his drawings started to appear in *The New Yorker*. One of the most famous showed a husband and wife in bed, and behind them, with his flippers resting on the headboard, a seal. The wife was saying, "All right, have it your way—you heard a seal bark!" Robert Benchley sent Thurber a congratulatory telegram about this cartoon, and Thurber was so pleased that he titled his first book of drawings *The Seal in the Bedroom*. Among Thurber's stories are two classics: "The Secret Life of Walter Mitty" and "The Catbird Seat." Both were made into movies, starring respectively Danny Kaye and Peter Sellers. Thurber reminisces about his wild youth in Columbus in *My Life and Hard Times*. He is also famous for inventing a unique species of dog, known as the Thurberdog, which may be viewed along with some other drawings and writings in his books *The Thurber Carnival*, *Thurber's Dogs*, *Alarms and Diversions*, and *Fables for Our Time*. Thurber's *The Years with Ross* is a hilarious biography of the first editor of *The New Yorker* and the hectic early years of that magazine.

A midget actually did play for a major league baseball team. His name was Eddie Gaedel, and he was three-feet, seven-inches tall and weighed in at sixty-five pounds. He was signed by Bill Veeck, manager of the St. Louis Browns, one of the worst ball clubs in history. In 1951, to get publicity and spur attendance, Veeck signed Eddie Gaedel to a contract and sent him in as a pinch hitter against the Detroit Tigers. Following instructions, Gaedel took four pitches and walked (his strike zone was one and a half inches high) . But the Browns lost anyway. Veeck said that he was accused of stealing the idea from Thurber, but that he actually stole it from John J. McGraw, manager of the New York Giants. McGraw employed a small hunchbacked man around the Giant clubhouse, for good luck, and he used to swear that one day he would send the little man up to bat, although he never did.